A TEACHER CALLED NICODEMUS

KENNETH A. WINTER

WildernessLessons

JOIN MY READERS' GROUP FOR UPDATES AND FUTURE RELEASES

Please join my Readers' Group so i can send you a free book, as well as updates and information about future releases, etc.

See the back of the book for details on how to sign up.

A Teacher Called Nicodemus

"The Called" - Book 3 (a series of novellas)

Published by:

Kenneth A. Winter

WildernessLessons, LLC

Richmond, Virginia

United States of America

kenwinter.org

wildernesslessons.com

Edited by Sheryl Martin Hash

Cover design by Scott Campbell Design

ISBN 978-1-7367155-9-8 (soft cover)

ISBN 978-1-9568660-0-1 (e-book)

ISBN 978-1-9568660-1-8 (large print)

Library of Congress Control Number: 2021924987

DEDICATION

Do nothing from selfish ambition or conceit, but in humility count others more significant than yourselves. Let each of you look not only to his own interests, but also to the interests of others. Have this mind among yourselves, which is yours in Christ Jesus.
Philippians 2:3-5 (ESV)

~

In memory of my friend, Albert "Pete" Peterson,
a giant of a man, spiritually and physically,
who humbly served the Lord as Billy Sunday's advance man
and always made this little boy feel like he was the most important person in the room.

~

CONTENTS

FROM THE AUTHOR

A word of explanation for those of you who are new to my writing.

You will notice that whenever i use the pronoun "I" referring to myself, i have chosen to use a lowercase "i." This only applies to me personally (in the Preface). i do not impose my personal conviction on any of the characters in this book. It is not a typographical error. i know this is contrary to proper English grammar and accepted editorial style guides. i drive editors (and "spell check") crazy by doing this. But years ago, the Lord convicted me – personally – that in all things i must decrease and He must increase.

And as a way of continuing personal reminder, from that day forward, i have chosen to use a lowercase "i" whenever referring to myself. Because of the same conviction, i use a capital letter for any pronoun referring to God throughout the entire book. The style guide for the New Living Translation (NLT) does not share that conviction. However, you will see that i have intentionally made that slight revision and capitalized any pronoun referring to God in my quotations of Scripture from the NLT. If i have violated any style guides as a result, please accept my apology, but i must honor this conviction.

Lastly, regarding this matter – this is a <u>personal</u> conviction – and i share it only so you will understand why i have chosen to deviate from normal editorial practice. i am in no way suggesting or endeavoring to have anyone else subscribe to my conviction. Thanks for your understanding.

PREFACE

~

This fictional novella is part of a series titled, *The Called*, which is about ordinary people whom God called to use in extraordinary ways. We tend to elevate the people we read about in Scripture and place them on a pedestal far beyond our reach. We often think, "Of course God used them. They had extraordinary strength or extraordinary faith. But God could never use an ordinary person like me."

That is a lie the evil one desires us to believe. He loves for us to think we can't possibly be used by God because we are too ordinary. But the reality is God has used the ordinary to accomplish the extraordinary throughout history – and He has empowered them to do so through His Holy Spirit.

This story is about the life of one of those ordinary people – Nicodemus, the teacher. Though Nicodemus was a learned teacher, and a member of the elite ruling body called the Sanhedrin, he appears to have been a very humble man. The first time we see him in Scripture, he is coming to Jesus as an honest seeker. Most of the other religious leaders who came to Jesus with questions did so with an arrogant determination to catch Him in a trap. Nicodemus, however, appears to have had no agenda except to sincerely understand who Jesus was and the truth He was teaching.

Their conversation includes one of the best known verses in the Bible – John 3:16 – which is the very essence of the Gospel message: *For this is how God loved the world: He gave His one and only Son, so that everyone who believes in Him will not perish but have eternal life.*[1]

Nicodemus is only mentioned in the Gospel of John. Bear in mind that John only recorded events in his Gospel account that he personally witnessed. That would indicate he was in the room that night when Jesus and Nicodemus spoke. It is also reasonable to assume that John and Nicodemus previously knew one another. Given his position, Nicodemus was taking a chance coming in secret to speak with Jesus. He would have needed a trusted intermediary to set up the meeting.

John also mentions Nicodemus on two other occasions. The second time we see him is when he questions the motives of the religious leaders.[2] That is where we learn Nicodemus was a Galilean. I have chosen Capernaum as his hometown and created a back story about why he grew up in that village. The Bible does not tell us where he was from in Galilee. Placing him in Capernaum created interesting story possibilities regarding his interaction with others who lived in that small fishing village.

The third time we see Nicodemus is when he assists Joseph of Arimathea in the burial of Jesus's body. Again, John's reference suggests he and Nicodemus had more than just a passing knowledge of one another.

It is reasonable to conclude that Nicodemus became a follower of Jesus, though Scripture does not tell us definitively. By assisting in the burial of Jesus's body, both Joseph and Nicodemus put their positions on the Sanhedrin in jeopardy. They would have found themselves alienated and ostracized by the other leaders who had participated in the plot to crucify Jesus. Church tradition also supports the belief that both men became followers of Jesus.

Over the years, i have become intrigued by this humble man who was willing to take great risk to seek out and then stand for the truth. An adage attributed to Alexander Hamilton says, "if you don't stand for something, you will fall for anything." Nicodemus appears to have been one of those men who stood boldly for truth. We, as twenty-first century followers of Jesus, would do well to follow his example.

Obviously, i have taken liberties in developing a "back story" about Nicodemus. i do so in an effort for us to see him as a real person – a son with a family history, more than likely a loving husband and father, and a man who became recognized by others as a leader.

So, i hope you will sit back and enjoy this walk through Nicodemus's life. Many of the characters in the story come directly from Scripture, though their connection with Nicodemus is on multiple occasions either conjecture or completely fictional. You will easily recognize those characters. In some instances, i have chosen to add background details about them that are also either fictional or conjectures not confirmed in Scripture. i have also added fictional characters to round out the narrative. In the back of the book is a listing of characters to help you work through what is historical fact and what is fiction.

Throughout the story, some instances of dialogue are direct quotes from Scripture. When quoting Scripture, you will find i have italicized it. The Scripture references are included in a bibliography in the back of the book. Dialogue not italicized is part of the fictional story that helps advance the narrative.

In conclusion, my prayer is you will see Nicodemus through new eyes as you read this ... and be challenged to live out your walk with Jesus with the same boldness and courage he displayed. And most importantly, i pray you will be challenged to be an "ordinary" follower with the willingness and faith to be used by God in extraordinary ways ... for His glory!

∾

1

MY GREAT-GREAT-GREAT
GRANDFATHER NAHUM

~

*T*he two friends stood their ground in the midst of overwhelming odds. They had already seen many of their own number fall that day. Now it was late afternoon as they watched the enemy continue to advance. One of the men, Nahum, called out to the other, "Judas, I will stand with you and fight on this field as long as Jehovah God continues to give me strength!"

"Nahum, there is no one else I would rather have fighting here by my side!" Judas replied. Suddenly he shouted, "Watch out there, behind you!"

Nahum turned, and his blade met the enemy just in the nick of time – as it had many times before. "Judas, only a handful of us remain, and the enemy continues to push forward. Most of our men have either fled or lie dead here on the battlefield."

"Nahum, we will trust Jehovah God to grant us victory! He will not forsake us! But if my life is required as a part of the price for that victory, I will gladly lay it down here and now!"

"Judas!" Nahum shouted. But at that moment, Nahum saw his friend fall to his death. An enemy blade had pierced his heart ... and moments later Nahum fell to that same fate.

In many respects, my story begins with those two friends who fought side by side that day. My name is Nicodemus, and Nahum was my great-great-great grandfather. He was a priest who fought bravely alongside Judas Maccabeus in what ultimately became a successful revolt against the Seleucid Empire.

Our nation had been under the control of pagan conquerors for over 500 years – far longer than we had endured the slavery of Egypt. Our people were taken captive by the Assyrians about 700 years ago, followed in succession by the Babylonians, the Persians, and the Greeks. At the time Nahum died, our people were under the rule of the Seleucid Greeks. If those years taught our people anything, it was that none of our captors had any regard for the God of Abraham, Isaac, and Jacob.

Throughout the 500 years of captivity, we had seen our worship continually restricted and our temple repeatedly desecrated. The Seleucids were no exception. It was their blasphemous desecration of our temple in Jerusalem that prompted a priest named Mattathias, along with his five sons, to lead our people in revolt against the Seleucids.

One year into that revolt, Mattathias died from injuries he received in battle. Just before he died, he designated his third son, Judas, to replace him as leader. Everyone, including his brothers, agreed that Judas was best suited for the role, having witnessed his valor in battle and his decisive military skills.

Though the Seleucid army was far superior to the small Judean force in number and in training, Judas's decision to employ guerilla warfare tactics gave the Jews a slight advantage. My ancestor Nahum quickly rose in the Judean ranks due to his bravery and fighting skills. He soon became one of Judas's most trusted commanders.

One day, Judas directed Nahum to lead 3,000 men to attack the Seleucid outposts scattered throughout Galilee and to free the Jews living in those settlements. Jehovah God granted him favor, and they achieved great victory. From there, they advanced on the forces in Gilead and the settlements east of the Jordan River. Fighting continued for six years, during which time both sides suffered defeats and casualties. But still, our people continued to trust that God would ultimately bring them victory.

Seven years into the fighting, the Seleucid King Demetrius determined to put down the Maccabean revolt once and for all. He dispatched 20,000 of his infantry and 2,000 of his cavalry to lay siege to Jerusalem. Judas and Nahum brought their forces together on that battlefield. They were overwhelmingly outnumbered, and many of their men deserted. But those two leaders, together with just under 1,000 soldiers, stood firm until they were brought to death by the swords of their enemy.

Their bravery became an inspiration to the Jews. Judas's brothers assumed command and, after several more years of fighting, defeated the Seleucids. Judea was finally freed from foreign rule – at least for a period of eighty years, until the Roman general Pompey laid siege to Jerusalem.

Those eighty years of freedom between the rules of the Seleucids and the Romans are known in our history as the Hasmonean dynasty. Judas's younger brother, Simon, became the first Hasmonean leader and high priest. Upon his death, he was followed by a succession of his descendants.

The Hasmoneans chose to honor the memory of my great-great-great-grandfather and reward his bravery by bestowing tributes upon his descendants. Those tributes greatly impacted each subsequent generation of our family … including me.

～

2

A VILLAGE ESTABLISHED IN HIS HONOR

~

ollowing the defeat of the Seleucids, the Hasmonean kings realized towns and villages needed be established throughout the wilderness lands north of Jerusalem if the Jewish nation was going to maintain its independence. King John Hyrcanus I appointed my great-great-grandfather Adir to lead the effort by establishing a new fishing settlement on the northern shore of the Sea of Galilee.

The king chose Adir because the settlement was to be named in honor of his father, Nahum, known for his military achievements in the region of Galilee. It was to be called Capernaum, meaning "Nahum's village."

The Hasmoneans also bestowed a financial tribute to Adir in honor of Nahum. A portion was designated to fund the settlement of the village, and the remainder was a gift to our family. Up until then, my ancestors had never enjoyed great wealth, but all that changed that day.

Adir, together with his family – his wife, Devorah, and their young son, Menahem – along with one hundred men, women, children, and their flocks, set out from Jerusalem to establish the new settlement.

After they had been traveling awhile, Devorah asked, "Husband, how long will it take us to arrive at this new place along the sea?"

"The king tells me it will require eight days considering the large number of animals and materials we are bringing with us," Adir replied. "So, it will be nine days before we arrive, counting the Sabbath day we will observe along the way."

"You and I have never lived outside of Jerusalem. What will we do when we arrive at this place in the wilderness?" Devorah asked, not for the first time.

"First, we will thank Jehovah God for our safe arrival and His great blessing and provision for our family," Adir answered. "And then we will jump into the sea and wash the dust from our travels off of our bodies!"

"But we don't know how to swim!" Devorah exclaimed. "We've never lived near a sea!"

"Then the second thing we will do, wife, is learn how to swim!" Adir responded with a grin.

Jehovah God had equipped this group of settlers with all the skills needed to establish the village. Once they arrived, several men, who were carpenters, quickly went to work constructing shelters for them to live in.

A handful of others were boat builders and fishermen. They began building the settlement's first two boats so the fishermen could get to work plying their trade. Fish would not only be a staple of their diets but also a primary source of the village's income.

Still others began cultivating portions of land that were best suited for growing crops. The land was fertile, and by the time the harvest season arrived, the settlers enjoyed a bountiful gathering of grain. Soon the plentiful olive crops followed. Gratefully, the oil and grain mills were finished just in time to receive the harvest.

Adir and the other men decided not to build a defensive wall around the settlement. Since the Lord had situated the village on the shores of the sea, they did not want to be partitioned off from its beauty or its natural breezes.

In addition to overseeing the development of the settlement, Adir made sure the synagogue was built and established in the center of everything. The village was thriving as the settlers marked the first anniversary in their new community, and more families had begun to arrive. The village now boasted a population of 200, including the small fighting force the Hasmonean king had sent with them for protection.

Adir gathered the people in and around the synagogue to commemorate that first anniversary with a time of praise and thanksgiving to Jehovah God. Sacrifices were offered to God, and the joy of the people could be heard from far away as Adir opened the Scriptures and read:

"Shout with joy to the Lord, O earth! Worship the Lord with gladness. Come before Him singing with joy. Acknowledge that the Lord is God! He made us, and we are His. We are His people, the sheep of His pasture.

"Enter His gates with thanksgiving; go into His courts with praise. Give thanks to Him and bless His name. For the Lord is good. His unfailing love continues forever, and His faithfulness continues to each generation."[1]

Then Adir went about the task of ensuring the continued welfare of his own family and the generations that would follow.

≈

3

A MERCHANT NAMED SHEBNA

∾

*S*oon after the Hasmoneans began to rule, our priests and teachers began to divide into two factions. The first was the Pharisees, who believed Jehovah God gave an oral law, or Talmud, in addition to the written law, the Torah. The oral law was given by God as a way to apply the written law. Another distinction was their belief that an afterlife exists. God punishes the wicked and rewards the righteous in the world to come.

The second faction was the Sadducees, consisting primarily of people of wealth or priestly position. They rejected the oral law and traditions, and insisted on a literal interpretation of the Torah. They also flatly denied the existence of an afterlife. Over the years, their beliefs were influenced by Greek philosophy and were considered liberal by the Pharisees.

My great-great-grandfather Adir was one of the first Pharisees, and each generation of my family since him has followed that same line of thought – including me. But while our religious beliefs aligned with the Pharisees, our status as wealthy merchants aligned more with the Sadducees. That turn of events mostly took place through Adir's grandson, Asher, who subsequently became my grandfather. Please allow me to explain.

Many Jews chose to remain in Babylon even after Persian King Artaxerxes granted permission for them to return to our homeland. And when the Seleucids seized power in the region, these Jews saw no advantage to leaving their adopted homes to return to a region under a more severe pagan control. But, when our people achieved their independence from the Seleucids through the revolt, many of the Jews in Babylon began to reconsider their options.

Three of those were brothers: Hillel, Shebna, and Camydus. You have probably heard of the oldest brother, Rabbi Hillel. He became a revered sage, scholar, and leader of our people. His youngest brother, Camydus, was also a respected leader. As a matter of fact, both had already achieved significant status before they left Babylon to migrate to Jerusalem.

The lesser known of the three brothers was Shebna. He was an astute merchant who had already begun to build his wealth in Babylon. Having a more adventurous spirit than his brothers, he decided to migrate to the emerging frontier of our people – specifically the village of Capernaum. When he arrived, he immediately sought out my grandfather, Asher, who by then had assumed the role as leader of our village from his father, Menahem.

My grandfather greeted Shebna by extending a hand of friendship, just as he did to all new families coming to Capernaum. "Shebna," he said, "welcome to our village! I am so grateful that Jehovah God has led you to settle here. Please let me know how I can assist you as you get your family settled."

"Asher, even though I have only just arrived, I have already learned you are the man who can be of greatest help to me as I establish here," Shebna warmly replied. "I am told you are a man of vision and great initiative. I, too, am such a man, and I know the Lord God has led me here to help further the prosperity of this village – and our two families."

"Then it would appear that we have much to discuss!" my grandfather responded.

The two men quickly became trusted friends and ardent business partners. When Rome subsequently conquered our land and placed Herod the Great as ethnarch (governor) over our people, they saw it as a major business opportunity.

Though our Hasmonean kings had led us to keep strict observance of God's laws, they had done little to further the economic health of our region. Herod, on the other hand, was committed to allowing us to worship God without pagan influence as well as bring about economic expansion. Shebna and Asher took full advantage of those fiscal plans.

Since Capernaum was located on the sea, they invested in building our harbor into a thriving seaport for trade with other parts of Galilee and Judea. Herod and the Romans obliged by constructing a major trade route called the Via Maris. It connected Damascus with Alexandria in Egypt and passed through Capernaum, as well as Herod's new city of Caesarea Maritima along the Mediterranean Sea. This meant many travelers, caravans, and traders began to pass through our village.

Shebna and Asher thrived in this new environment. Their mills produced most of the olive oil being exported from our village, and they built a warehouse on the shore where fish could be salted and dried for export. Soon they were the sole exporter of the fish caught daily by our local fishermen. Everything the two men touched seemed to turn into gold.

My grandfather was able to take the financial legacy given to Adir and passed down to him through his father, Menahem, and multiply it into much greater wealth. Shebna soon joined Asher as the other leading elder of our village; their two families occupied the largest homes in our settlement. One of those homes became my birthplace and has since passed from one generation to the next.

~

4

GROWING UP AS A SON OF MEANS IN A POSITION OF PRIVILEGE

~

$\mathcal{M}$y grandfather and Shebna's deep friendship and profitable business partnership lasted for the remainder of their lives. As a matter of fact, the two men planned for their sons, Yaakov and Ishmael, respectively, to follow in their footsteps and continue the partnership. The problem was that Yaakov had a different idea. At age fifteen, he approached my grandfather, Asher.

"Father," he said, "Jehovah God has not given me the passion for business He has given to you. I believe He has called me to become a rabbi – to teach His people the truths and ways of God. I fear that to do anything else would be disobedient to God. I do not want to disappoint you, but I also do not want to disobey God."

Though my grandfather was disappointed, he received the news with grace and compassion. "Yaakov, my son, I have only ever wanted the best for you. And doing what Jehovah God has placed before you to do – no matter what it is – will always be the best! If God is leading you to become a rabbi, then we must send you to Jerusalem to study the Scriptures under Shebna's brother, Rabbi Hillel."

Yaakov studied under the rabbi for five years. When his time was completed, he returned to Capernaum to serve as a rabbi in the local synagogue. Soon afterward, he became interested in a young woman he had known since they were children but who had blossomed during his absence. Her name was Nissa, and she was Shebna's daughter. To the delight of their parents, Yaakov and Nissa seemed to be drawn to each other – so the families wasted no time in arranging their marriage.

Soon afterward my grandfather declared, "Friends and family, though the next generation of Shebna's and my families will not be bound in a business partnership, our children will be bound through a marriage partnership that will carry forward to our future generations. And that is an even greater delight to us both! Instead of anticipating the financial profits our children could produce, we will look forward to the many grandchildren they will produce instead – and that is a much greater blessing!"

Shebna's son, Ishmael, showed a great talent for commerce and was put in charge of his father's business ventures. Asher and Shebna were both pleased with how the Lord had ordered their steps for the continued success of their future generations.

After several years, God blessed Yaakov and Nissa with a son, Nicodemus. And that is where my personal story begins. I enjoyed an idyllic life growing up in Capernaum along the Sea of Galilee. My family was well respected on both sides of my ancestral tree, and I was a son of means and privilege. My father was the respected rabbi of our village. And while I was still a young boy, he was selected by the men of the village to take a seat as a member of our local Sanhedrin.

Each city and town throughout the provinces of Judea, Galilee and Samaria selects up to twenty-three men to serve as judges to settle local disputes, make administrative decisions related to the village and oversee religious affairs requiring interpretation beyond the purview of the local rabbi. Affairs that cannot be settled by these local Sanhedrin are referred to the Great Sanhedrin in Jerusalem.

My father made sure I grew up knowing the teachings of the Torah from as far back as I can remember. He taught me to have not only a knowledge of God's Word but also a love for the God of the Word. He taught me to hide God's Word in my heart.

He often reminded me, "God spoke these words, saying, '*I am the Lord your God ..., you shall have no other gods before Me. I will show My favor to those who love Me and keep My commandments.*'"[1]

By the time I was fifteen, I knew God was leading me to follow in my father's footsteps to serve Him as a rabbi. I had been traveling to Jerusalem with my father to observe the annual feasts since I was twelve years old. Each time, as we approached the temple, I did so with great reverence and awe. But this time when I set off with my father for Jerusalem, it was harder because I knew I would be remaining there for several years to complete my studies.

We arrived just prior to the start of Sukkot, a celebration often referred to as the Feast of the Tabernacles. It is a time of joyful remembrance of God's deliverance, protection, provision, and faithfulness to our people – remembering the forty years He led us through the wilderness.

My father spotted Rabbi Hillel at the temple, and we walked over to him. "Teacher," my father began, "please allow me to introduce my son, Nicodemus. He has come to sit at your feet and learn from you, just as I did at his age. Nicodemus, this is your mother's uncle, Rabbi Hillel. There is no finer teacher in all of Israel. Listen to his every word and hold his teaching in your heart."

~

5

A SECOND-CLASS JEW IN JERUSALEM

~

*R*abbi Hillel frequently took his students to the temple where we would sit in one of the outer courtyards as he asked us questions. He was always patient with us, even though we often gave him incorrect answers. One morning he asked, "Who was the prophet Isaiah quoting when he wrote, *'The Spirit of the Sovereign Lord is upon Me, because the Lord has appointed Me to bring good news to the poor. He has sent Me to comfort the brokenhearted and to announce that captives will be released, prisoners will be freed, and the blind will see'*?"[1]

"He was writing of the Messiah who will come from the royal line of David," I responded.

Annas, one of my fellow students, quickly spoke up. "Teacher, you know our Hasmonean leaders questioned the accuracy of Isaiah's prophecy that the Messiah will be a descendant of David. The next thing Nicodemus will want us to believe is that the Messiah will also be a Galilean!"

Several of the talmidim (disciples) chuckled, but Rabbi Hillel looked at them disapprovingly. "The Hasmonean leaders discredited the prophecies of Isaiah in order to usurp the legitimate royal line of King David and legitimize their own ascension into the role," he said. "That is what motivated them to also seize the lawful priestly role of the Zadokites. Annas, you would do well to rightly interpret the Scriptures instead of blindly following in the footsteps of the Hasmoneans."

Several of the other talmidim now chuckled at Annas's expense. Rabbi Hillel also cast a disapproving glance their way before he continued. "And Annas, there is nothing to prevent the Messiah from being a Galilean. Be careful you do not use your own racial prejudices to shape your interpretation of Scripture. You may very well find yourself on the wrong side of the argument."

Hillel looked over at me after making that last statement. He was aware Annas and some of the other young men from Judea looked down on me, as well as the others who were from the province of Galilee. The rabbi knew some of that prejudice had been passed down to Annas from his grandfather, Camydus, who also happened to be the scholar's younger brother. The two brothers had often debated that subject.

Rabbi Hillel's own grandson, Gamaliel, was also in our group of talmidim. He and I usually agreed on most things, whereas I *disagreed* with Annas on most everything. Gamaliel was a Pharisee like me, and not surprisingly, Annas was a Sadducee. Though not all Sadducees shared Annas's prejudice toward Galileans, it didn't take me long to discover that many did.

As time passed, I discovered more of that prejudice in Jerusalem than I expected. Some of the looks and comments directed at me made me wish I could return to Capernaum. But I was grateful for the teaching of the rabbi; I was growing exponentially in my understanding of Scripture.

Instead of being called a student, those of us under his teaching were called a talmid. There is an important distinction between the two terms. A student seeks knowledge from the teacher to earn a grade, whereas a talmid wants to be truly like the teacher. Most of us wanted to follow in Rabbi Hillel's footsteps, though I questioned whether that was true of Annas and a few others.

It was obvious Annas was an ambitious young man. I heard him bragging on more than one occasion that he would become the youngest high priest in our history – and I had little doubt that would be the case.

Since we spent a lot of our time at the temple, we would often meet many of our religious leaders. The high priest at the time was a Sadducee named Simon ben Boethus. He had been in that position for thirteen years when I first arrived in Jerusalem. He seemed to enjoy the favor of the Romans, as well as Rome's appointed governor, King Herod.

As a matter of fact, Simon ben Boethus's daughter, Marianne, was Herod's current wife – his third. No one was certain whether it was Simon's influence through Marianne, or Herod's own sense of grandeur, but the ethnarch was having the temple renovated to rival or eclipse its appearance at the time of King Solomon. There was no denying the impressiveness of the work and the attention to detail.

One of the additions being made was the Hall of Hewn Stones, constructed as a meeting place for the Great Sanhedrin. It was built into the north wall of the temple with half of the hall extending into the sanctuary and the other half extending outside. With doorways in both directions, it symbolized the authority the Great Sanhedrin had over all aspects of our lives – both religious and civil. It truly was a corridor of power.

Though my father was a member of our local Sanhedrin in Capernaum, those members did not command the same respect and power as the members of this Great Sanhedrin. I equated the local group as being servants and this group as being rulers – even though I knew that wasn't the case across the board.

I suspected that many of the teachers and religious leaders in Jerusalem held their positions because of the power they sought and not a desire to worship or serve God. I was grateful that Rabbi Hillel was an exception. But I was still thankful to the Lord when my time finally arrived to return to Capernaum.

6

THE LEADING RABBI OF CAPERNAUM

~

"Welcome home, my son!" my father called out, even before I arrived at the door.

"It is so good to be home, father!" I said as we embraced. "I have missed the smells and sounds of the sea."

My father looked at me and smiled. "When you greet your mother, I hope you will also tell her that you missed the taste of her good cooking and the comforts of her company!"

"Of course, father, that goes without saying," I said matter-of-factly.

"Perhaps, but make sure you say it!"

I could tell by the twinkle in his eye that he was teasing, but I also knew I would be wise to heed his advice. I honestly had not realized how much I missed him and my mother until that moment. I would not be in any hurry to leave them or my beloved Capernaum any time soon.

As we sat down to catch up, I remarked to my father how much the village had grown during my absence. "The number of fishing boats appears to have doubled, and I saw there were many more children playing along the shore."

"Yes," he responded, "Jehovah God is leading more people to our village. We are pushing out one of the walls of the synagogue to accommodate more people. The footprint of the village is expanding, and your Uncle Ishmael tells me the family business is prospering. God has been very good to the people of Capernaum."

The conversation then turned to my time in Jerusalem. I told my father how Rabbi Hillel's teachings had expanded my thinking and deepened my understanding of the Scriptures. I also told him about the religious leaders I had met, as well as some of my fellow students, who were focused only on the worldly desires of position and power.

"Father, I pray God will turn the hearts of many of our leaders back to Him," I said, "and we will truly become a people who seek Him with our whole hearts, souls, and minds."

"Well, always remember, my son," he wisely replied, "it must also be true of us. Make sure you stay rightly oriented before our Lord, seeking to love Him and honor Him with your whole being. Ask Him to keep you from becoming distracted by the words and actions of those around you – no matter how godly they may want you to believe they are!"

Just then my mother entered the room. She had been away tending to a sick neighbor, and she looked tired. I remembered my father's advice and told her how much I had missed her – which was true because I truly had!

Over the next few days, I savored the time with my parents, family, and friends as they stopped by to welcome me home. We laughed together and shared wonderful memories, and I entertained them with stories about the great city of Jerusalem.

As the days passed, I noticed my mother becoming weak and frail. By the end of the week she had developed a high fever. Apparently, she had contracted our sick neighbor's illness. The village midwife prepared an herbal remedy, but it did not help. One week later – several days after our neighbor died – my mother died, as well.

My father was inconsolable. Gratefully, Uncle Ishmael made all the burial arrangements so I could tend to my father. But he refused to eat. Nothing I said eased his anguish. After two days, I realized his sorrow was masking his physical pain and fever. The midwife began to treat him for the same illness my mother had battled. But her efforts again proved to be in vain. My father died – exactly one week after my mother.

The joy I felt the day I returned home now seemed like a distant memory. In less than a month I had lost both my parents; I was overcome with grief. Though I was grateful God had given me a few weeks with them before they died, I had always thought we would have many more years together. People in our village joined me in mourning. They had lost their beloved rabbi and his devoted wife.

Gratefully, the illness did not spread through our village; it was limited to my parents and our neighbor. But my parents' deaths left a huge hole in the hearts of our entire community.

Someone needed to step into my father's shoes and minister to our friends and neighbors. Someone needed to speak God's truth to hearts that were hurting. That responsibility fell to me. I soon became the leading rabbi of Capernaum. It was not a position I sought; it was a position that sought me.

∼

7

GOD GIVES ME A FAMILY

~

*W*hile I was ministering to the people of our village, my Uncle Ishmael and his family took on the responsibility of ministering to me. Though our families had always been close, my parents' deaths brought us even closer. Ishmael became more than a business partner, friend, and uncle – he became a surrogate father, and his family embraced me as one of their own.

Ishmael's daughters – Salome, three years my elder, and Tali, five years my junior – had been like sisters to me growing up. In fact, Tali was the little sister who far too often we ignored! But since I'd been home, I saw Tali in a whole new light.

Her tenderness and her beauty had blossomed while I was away. I didn't quite know what to do with these new feelings. I regretted all those years I had cast her aside as an annoying little girl, but I had far too many responsibilities now to give her any attention.

I wasn't the only man with feelings for one of Uncle Ishmael's daughters. A young fisherman from Bethsaida named Zebedee was spending a great deal of time in Capernaum – particularly in the presence of Salome. He said it was because he was selling the fish he and his partner Jonah caught each day to Uncle Ishmael at the fish packing warehouse. But obviously his interests in Capernaum extended well beyond his fishing trade!

It wasn't long before Salome and Uncle Ishmael both confided in me that a marriage agreement was being considered. Of course, Uncle Ishmael seemed more hesitant than Salome; after all, she was his eldest daughter, and no one would ever measure up in his eyes to be worthy of her. But even I could see Zebedee was an honorable man who strived to be righteous before God. He was a hard worker and would be a good provider. He obviously had deep feelings for Salome and she for him. Eventually my uncle agreed to their marriage.

As the rabbi of the village, I was privileged to conduct their marriage ceremony. Though Salome moved away to Bethsaida, the happy couple visited Capernaum often. It was a delight to see how their relationship continued to grow – and to rejoice with them one year later when God blessed them with a son, James.

Life in the village continued to thrive, and more people were added to our number each week. More people also meant more opportunities for ministry. My work continued to increase. I was engaged in ministry from dawn to dusk with little time for anything else.

However, I occasionally took solitary walks along the Sea of Galilee to clear my head. These were times when I could speak with Jehovah God without any distractions or interruptions. It was during one of these walks that God spoke to me through another's voice.

"Good afternoon, Rabbi!" I heard a voice call out.

I had not realized anyone was walking behind me, so her voice startled me. I knew even before I turned around it was Tali. She saw my obvious surprise.

"Good afternoon, Tali," I replied. "Please forgive me for not realizing you were there. I am afraid you caught me deep in thought."

She looked at me with a playful smile. "You apparently have been deep in thought for many weeks now because you haven't said two words to me in as many months. Even when you come to our home for dinner you seem preoccupied when you are near me. Have I done something to offend you?"

"No, not at all!" I said hastily as I struggled to find the right words. I was more tongue-tied around her than I had been in front of Rabbi Hillel! "I must apologize for my behavior. Each day I spend all my time and energy ministering to the people of our village. Regrettably, I often have little of either left to share with those who are closest to me. Please forgive my lack of attention!"

"Do you think of me as one of those closest to you?" she asked with a shy smile.

Her question took me off guard. For months I had denied my feelings for Tali and had foolishly barricaded them behind a wall of silence toward her. Her question was causing that wall to crack, and I blushed at the thought of how I truly felt about her.

Hesitantly, I answered. "Yes, I do, Tali. I am so sorry I have not acted in a way that showed you how I feel toward you. When we were young, I always treated you like a little child undeserving of my attention. But now that we are older, it is I who has behaved like a little child not expressing my feelings toward you."

"So, you have feelings toward me?" she said coyly.

We stood in silence as her mouth slowly formed a tender smile. I could feel my face turning bright red. For the first, and perhaps the last time in my life, I was at a loss for words. So, I just continued my walk along the shore in silence – but now with Tali walking by my side.

∼

8

GOD CONTINUES TO BLESS OUR FAMILY

∼

 *S*ix months later, Tali became my wife. Ishmael, who was not only my uncle but now my father-in-law, too, was overjoyed to bless our union. He shared with me awhile later that God had assured him Tali and I would have a son who would one day take over the family business enterprise. I told Ishmael we would see if God blessed us with a son, and if so, how He would lead the boy in the future. Each time Ishmael would reply, "Yes, we will see!"

Words cannot express the joy God brought into my life through Tali. I had told the story of creation many times, but it was only after she and I were married that I fully understood what the Lord God meant when He said, *"It is not good for the man to be alone. I will make a helper as his complement."*[1]

We had been married for one year when our daughter Leah was born. Ishmael was somewhat disappointed the baby was not a boy. But he quickly got over it! Leah not only took after her mother in appearance but also in temperament. She quickly had her father – and her grandfather – wrapped around her little finger!

A year after that we welcomed our son, Reuben. Ishmael wasted no time in again reminding me of God's promise.

"It is a little too soon to make that decision, Ishmael," I told him. "We will see how the Lord God directs Reuben's steps when he is old enough to make that decision on his own."

To which Ishmael smiled and again replied, "Yes, we will see!"

Two years later our daughter Rebekah was born. Tali and I could not contain our joy over the many ways God was blessing our family. Friends and neighbors often told us God was blessing us because of our righteousness before Him. And as a rabbi who was still young, I often acknowledged their statements in a way that affirmed that belief.

But that all changed when Rebekah was fourteen months old. We awoke one morning to discover Rebekah had died in her sleep. There was no physician living in our village; local midwives always treated any illnesses or injuries. But they could not explain what had caused Rebekah's death.

I began to question what Tali and I had possibly done to deserve this punishment from God. If our blessings were the result of our works of righteousness, it only stood to reason that Rebekah's death was caused by our unrighteousness! Though they did not say it to us directly, it was obvious some of our friends and neighbors thought the same thing.

In the midst of our grief the Lord God began to lovingly correct me in my misunderstanding of His ways. He led me to the writings in the books of poetry, beginning with Ecclesiastes. He reminded me our lives contain a mixture of joy and sorrow, pleasure and pain, life and death. Each is a part of the season of life. He inspired me to teach these truths to our neighbors when we next gathered at the synagogue.

I told them, "The Lord has reminded me through His servant Job who lost everything: *'The Lord gave me everything I had, and the Lord has taken it away. Still I will praise the name of the Lord.'*[(2)]

"There will be seasons that are difficult for us to understand. We will not comprehend why God has permitted it. I am only beginning to grasp this with the death of my little daughter.

"The painful parts of our lives are the result of the sin that entered into this world through Adam and Eve. But our God is not a vindictive God. He does not send death and calamity to punish us. As the psalmist King David wrote when he was walking through grief, *'Even when I walk through the dark valley of death, I will not be afraid, for the Lord is close beside me. His rod and His staff comfort me.'*[(3)]

"As a matter of fact, He has promised us through his prophet Isaiah that He is sending One who will swallow up death forever and wipe away all our tears. In the meantime, we must trust Him as He is fulfilling His purpose in His timeframe. Perhaps ours will be the generation that welcomes the arrival of the Messiah. Perhaps ours will be the generation who sees death defeated.

"Until then, Tali and I will continue to bow before Him and say, 'We praise the name of the Lord,' and we will thank Him for the fourteen months He gave us with Rebekah and for the blessing of Leah and Reuben."

The Lord God did not choose to give us any additional children. He did permit us to help nurture many children who were a part of our village – some of whom became as close to us as our own Leah, Reuben, and Rebekah.

∼

9

TWO PROMISING STUDENTS

~

*O*ne of those children was a boy whose family had been intertwined with mine for many years. When my grandfathers, Asher and Shebna, began their business partnership, they needed a carpenter to oversee the construction of their warehouses and mills, as well as their homes. They hired a craftsman named Uziel.

When my Uncle Ishmael took over the business, he employed Uziel's grandson, Betzalel, to build whatever was needed for our family's business enterprises. Betzalel was a gifted craftsman who would have made a handsome living in Jerusalem. But, like his father and grandfather before him, he chose to remain in Capernaum and enjoy the idyllic life along the sea.

Betzalel's eldest son was a young man named Jairus. He was four years old when I returned to Capernaum from Jerusalem. I discovered he had an insatiable hunger to learn. Growing up, he demonstrated he could recall the Scriptures better than those who were twice his age. And on more than one occasion he posed a question to this rabbi that caused me to dig deep for the answer.

"Rabbi, why did Jehovah God accept Abel's offering but reject Cain's offering?" he asked one day. "Were they not both the fruits of their labor – Cain's as the gift of a farmer and Abel's as the gift of a shepherd?"

"We now know what God requires," I replied, "but back then Cain and Abel did not have benefit of the law. How were they to know what would be acceptable to God? Was God saying the fruits of the shepherd were better than the fruits of the farmer? Then what did that mean for the carpenters or the fishermen?"

My fellow talmidim and I had once had that same conversation with Rabbi Hillel, but we had been twice Jairus's age when the thought crossed our minds!

"Some would tell you," I continued, "that God rejected Cain's offering because there had been no shedding of blood, which was required for the angel of death to pass over the homes of the Jews that night in Egypt. But there is nothing in Scripture to indicate God had established that require-ment those many years before.

"Others would say Cain brought an offering of inferior fruits and vegeta-bles. But again, there is nothing in Scripture to tell us that.

"The simple truth is God knew what was in Cain's heart. It wasn't the condition of his gift; it was the condition of his heart. And Cain's imme-diate reaction of anger toward God revealed what was clearly already there!

"We would do well to remember that truth ourselves. It is not the size of the gift we bring to God; rather, it is the condition of our heart. God is not impressed with what we give but how we give it. There are many whose hearts are as hard as stone who are walking into the temple in Jerusalem today presenting gifts that appear to be grand. But God is no more accepting of those meaningless offerings than He was of Cain's."

There was an even younger boy among the students that day listening to our conversation. He was my nephew John – the youngest son of my sister-in-law, Salome. Though they did not live in Capernaum, John always came to the synagogue whenever his family was in the village.

Jairus and John became my best students, and their lives reflected this important truth: "First and foremost, we are to love God because He first loved us. Yes, He gave us the law, but He gave it to us because He loves us. We do not obey the law to earn His love; we obey His law because He loves us, and we love Him. Be careful you do not do what others have done. Do not turn the law from the blessing God intended it to be and turn it into a burden. Do not lose your joy under the weight of the law man has corrupted. Seek the Lord God with all of your hearts, souls, and minds!"

Eventually I knew I had taught these young men as much as I could. I recommended to their families that the boys be sent to the School of Hillel in Jerusalem for more training. By the time Jairus made the journey, his father knew his son would not follow in his footsteps as a carpenter. God was leading him to become a rabbi.

Since John was younger than Jairus, a few more years passed before he left for Jerusalem. In fact, by the time he arrived, Hillel's grandson Gamaliel was the teacher. But John did not stay there long. He was not studying to become a rabbi, though he understood God's Word better than most talmidim. He planned to continue assisting his father, Zebedee, on their family's fishing boats. But something told me God was going to use this fisherman in a different way – a way that would have great impact for generations to come.

～

10

SERVING IN OUR LOCAL SANHEDRIN

~

*W*e were beginning to hear rumors that our village's growth and prosperity were attracting Rome's attention – though we had rarely seen a Roman official or soldier. Nonetheless, Galilee remained under the authority of Herod Antipas, who had taken over as governor when his father, Herod the Great, died. It seemed Rome would not interfere with us as long as we continued to send them our taxes through our new tax collector, Matthew.

When Antipas became ruler, he began the development of a new Galilean capital, Tiberias, on the western shore of the Sea of Galilee. It was located about a day's journey south of Capernaum over land or half a day by sea. All the new construction and expansion ushered prosperity into the entire region, including Capernaum.

I had now been serving as a member of our local Sanhedrin for almost twenty-five years. I took my father's place on the council soon after he died. During that time our village had more than tripled in size. Though the growth had brought greater wealth, it had also brought greater conflict – most of which Antipas and Rome left for our local Sanhedrin to resolve.

When our citizens had a dispute they could not settle on their own, they would bring it before our Sanhedrin. Most often, the disputes had to do with finances. Sometimes they involved accusations between two parties over whether a Jewish law had been violated. On rare occasions, accusations involving criminal acts were brought before us. Gratefully, the latter were very rare.

On those extremely rare instances when we could not resolve a dispute, we would refer the matter to the Great Sanhedrin in Jerusalem. That body is comprised of seventy-one members from throughout the region. Serving on that council is a full-time responsibility.

Since all of us on the local council also had other duties, we would meet only when necessary. When I first began to serve, we convened once each month; now we were meeting once a week at the end of a workday. It made for a very long day.

While many of the disagreements brought before us were rather mundane, one particular one stands out. It was a complaint made by a husband about his new wife.

The husband stood before our council and declared, "After having slept with my wife on our wedding night, I found that she had slept with another man. I discovered she was not a virgin when we married. She must be stoned to death for the disgrace she has caused me."

Then the woman's father stood and said, "I gave my daughter to this man to be his wife, and now he has decided he no longer wants to be married to her. He is accusing her of shameful things – claiming she was not a virgin when he married her – simply to end their marriage contract."

Speaking on behalf of the council, I turned to the father and said, "Do you have any proof of her virginity at the time of their marriage?"

"Yes, I do," the father replied. "Here is the proof for all to see! This is the cloth from their wedding bed on the night their marriage was consummated!"

As we stared at the cloth, we quickly came to a decision. I turned to the husband to issue our verdict. "We find you guilty of making a false accusation against your wife and before this council. You have falsely accused a virgin of Israel. You will pay the woman's father the sum of one hundred pieces of silver. The woman will remain your wife and you may never divorce her. Do not ever let us hear you have done anything in retaliation against her, or it is you who will be taken to the edge of the village to be stoned to death!"[1]

Whether disputes were the result of false allegations like this one, or simply misunderstandings like most of them, our duty was to bring about resolution, judgment, or reparation for everyone.

One day I received a message from Jerusalem. A member of the Great Sanhedrin from the province of Galilee had died. I had been selected to take his seat on the council. Though the message came in the form of a request, it was not one I could decline. I truly had no interest in leaving my home and going back to Jerusalem, but apparently Jehovah God had other plans for me.

I was grateful I had continued to mentor Jairus after he returned home from his studies in Jerusalem. He had developed into a wise and godly leader. I did not hesitate to name him as my replacement as chief rabbi of the village. I could not have possibly thought any more highly of him. After all ... I had permitted him to marry my daughter, Leah, a few years earlier ... and now he was the father of my granddaughter, Ilana!

~

11

CHOSEN TO SERVE IN THE GREAT SANHEDRIN

~

*I*t was with sadness that Tali and I left our family behind in Capernaum and moved to Jerusalem. Our son, Reuben had become a very capable businessman under his grandfather's tutelage and was progressing nicely in his ability to manage the day-to-day affairs of the family's enterprise. Ishmael and I both knew the future of the business would be in good hands under his leadership.

The one we regretted leaving most of all was our precious little grand-daughter. We would miss watching Ilana as she grew. And we knew we would dearly miss the people of our village. They had become such a part of our lives over the years. But I knew Jehovah God in His sovereignty had placed this position in the Great Sanhedrin before me. I was not drawn by the power or prestige of the position; rather, I was going to serve and honor my Lord God by serving His people.

We traveled by cart with enough possessions to establish a small house-hold in Jerusalem. It took us a little more than four days to make the journey. We were glad when we finally entered the city walls through the Fish Gate on the northern wall.

Though I had lived in the city as a student, and Tali and I had been here on multiple occasions to commemorate our annual feasts, it felt different that day. We had a sense of foreboding that somehow our lives would never be the same. Some may have said it was because of the responsibility I was about to assume on the high council, but Tali and I both sensed it was more than that – we just didn't know what.

We made our way to the Hall of Hewn Stones. Tali went to the Women's Court in the temple while I entered the hall. Soon afterward I heard a familiar voice say, "Does anyone else smell the pungent odor of fresh fish? Either some delivery person has mistaken our chamber for the kitchen, or our newest member from Galilee has just arrived to take his seat among us! Ah, yes, I see it is the latter. Join me in welcoming Nicodemus of Capernaum into our midst!"

I knew before I spotted him it was my fellow talmid Annas. Twenty-eight years had passed since we had sat at the feet of Rabbi Hillel, but he had obviously not changed his opinion of people from Galilee. Annas had gone on to become the youngest high priest in our history. He had served in that role for nine years but had since been succeeded by one of his sons and then by his son-in-law Caiaphas, who was the current high priest.

Several other men were standing with him. The smirks on their faces showed they shared Annas's low opinion of Galileans. Their appearance confirmed that they, too, were Sadducees, one of them obviously being the current high priest.

"Thank you for your greeting, Annas," I replied. "I see that you are still as gracious and cordial as ever!"

But before Annas could respond, the current high priest spoke up. "Nicodemus, forgive my father-in-law's poor attempt at humor. We do welcome you into our midst, and we are grateful that you chose to accept the appointment. I know our families share much in common. And though our lives have followed different paths, Jehovah God has brought all of us together at this time and in this place to serve Him. So again, welcome to you, our fellow brother within the Sanhedrin."

Though his comments were much more gracious than his father-in-law's, I knew that as high priest he needed to be more diplomatic and politically savvy. I was fairly confident that underneath his polished façade were the same prejudices and biases of his father-in-law.

Caiaphas introduced me to the other men who were standing with him. Three of the men were Annas's sons – Eleazar, Jonathan, and Theophilus. Two others were also former high priests – Ishmael and Simon. It was obvious, even at this first meeting, that these men wielded great power within the Sanhedrin.

We were interrupted by another familiar voice who approached me from behind saying, "Hello, old friend! It is so good to see you!"

I was pleased to see Gamaliel as he reached out to embrace me – somewhat to the surprise of the other men. But I knew this fellow Pharisee was being sincere.

"Hello, my friend," I replied. "I have been looking forward to seeing you! I have much for which to thank you, including the way you trained up your talmid, Jairus. He is now the chief rabbi in our village, as well as my son-in-law. Thank you for your investment in him. He has made excellent use of the training you poured into him."

"I cannot take all of the credit," Gamaliel responded. "He came to me with a solid foundation in the Scriptures – and I know that was a result of your training. So, I thank you for sending him to me!"

Gamaliel pointed to the Pharisee who was accompanying him and said, "Nicodemus, allow me to introduce Joseph of Arimathea. I am certain you two will become good friends in the days ahead."

After I spent some time of getting better acquainted, I was directed to the home chosen for Tali and me. It was located in the upper city, not far from where all these other men lived. I excused myself and set out to find Tali so we could make our way to our new home.

12

ADJUSTING TO LIFE IN JERUSALEM

$\sim$

*L*ife in Jerusalem was very different from Capernaum. In Capernaum, everyone knew everyone else; there was little to no pretense. There was very little class consciousness. Though I had been the chief rabbi of the village, a member of the local Sanhedrin, and the living patriarch of one of the founding families – I never felt I was above anyone else.

The people of Capernaum all saw one another as friends and neighbors, though each of us had different responsibilities. But that was not the case in Jerusalem. The people here were very aware of everyone's social class because it was modeled and mandated by the religious leaders.

Most members of the Sanhedrin walked through the streets with an air of superiority, regardless of whether they were Pharisees or Sadducees. They projected to everyone around them that they were the unquestioned experts on the law, both in knowledge and practice. And whenever they spoke, prayed, presented offerings, or did any good deed, it was always done in public with great fanfare and exaggerated largesse.

I had been loved and admired by the people of our village in Capernaum. However, in Jerusalem I was feared and set apart from them. The only "friends" the Sanhedrin had were each other, and those relationships were only valued for the power or prestige derived from them.

While this was true of most members of the high council, there were exceptions. Gamaliel was particularly humble for a man revered as the most respected teacher of the law among those living. His grandfather, Hillel the Elder, would always be the most highly esteemed, but he had been dead now for over fifteen years.

Gamaliel did not teach about the stern and dispassionate God as many of our fellow members did; instead, he taught about a loving God we were to love, honor, and obey. But I quickly noticed that Gamaliel held a unique place of respect among all the members regardless of their position. They showed him great esteem and always paid him deference whenever he spoke.

Joseph of Arimathea was another member who demonstrated humility and love for God in all he did. He was often considered an outsider by other council members, much like I was. They rarely welcomed or embraced our opinions when we spoke up in meetings.

As a result, Tali and I often felt like outcasts in Jerusalem. Neither the other religious leaders nor the citizens befriended us due to the barriers of our station. For the most part, we were extremely lonely during our years living in the city. But still we knew God had led us into this role – for His purpose.

Our favorite times of the year in Jerusalem quickly became the annual festivals – not so much because of the reason for the feasts; but rather, because many of our friends from Capernaum would come to the city. The festivals became brief respites from the loneliness and isolation we other-wise felt.

Those times also provided an opportunity for us to catch up on news from home – and, even more, to enjoy time with our family when they came to celebrate the feasts. One such visit occurred the second fall after we had been in Jerusalem. Our family arrived for the Celebration of Sukkot.

"Papa and Mama," Leah said as they arrived, "I promised to embrace you and give you kisses from Reuben. He had planned to come himself as you know, but Grandfather Ishmael became sick the night before we set out on our journey. Reuben did not feel he could leave him, so he remained in Capernaum and told us to come ahead.

"The two of you may want to join us when we return in a few days so you can see grandfather yourselves. Reuben is sending word to Aunt Salome that she, too, should come and bring James and John with her."

"The illness sounds serious," Tali responded with a worried look on her face. "Should we go sooner?"

"The midwives believe he will still be with us for some time," Jairus answered, "but they also recommend the family come to see him within the next few weeks to say their final goodbyes. I think we will be fine if we remain here for the days of the festival and return when it is over."

"Then we will both return with you at the end of the week," I said.

"Aunt Salome will also need to get word to my cousin John," Leah added. "He has become the disciple of the one called John the baptizer. Apparently, my cousin is convinced this John is the one Isaiah said would come to announce the arrival of the Messiah. The baptizer is preaching and baptizing at the Jordan River. It will take a few days before they can get a message to John to come see grandfather in Capernaum."

"Then we will pray that Jehovah God will order our steps in a way that enables all of us to have time with Ishmael before He takes him home," I replied.

13

AN UNPLANNED TRIP TO CAPERNAUM

~

*T*en days later we arrived in Capernaum. Our joy at returning was overshadowed by our concern for Ishmael. Even though Leah had done her best to describe his condition, Tali and I were still not prepared for his appearance.

Although Ishmael was more than thirty years my senior, he had always had as much or more energy than I did. He never missed a day of work – other than the Sabbath or for a religious festival. I never knew him to spend a day in bed due to illness or injury. But now, he did not have the strength to raise himself in the bed.

The midwife told us she did not expect him to live out the week. She encouraged us all to express our goodbyes now while he could still hear us and respond. Tali and I went into his room together; suddenly, he seemed to have a burst of energy.

Ishmael raised himself and said, "Tali and Nicodemus, come near to me! My heart just leapt! Seeing you both brings me such great joy. It has been too long since these tired eyes have seen you. Come, sit with me, and tell me about your life in Jerusalem!"

Tali knelt beside his bed and took his hands in hers. "Papa, we will tell you, but first tell us how you feel."

"Tali, I am an old man," he said haltingly, "and for the first time in my life I feel like an old man. I have asked Jehovah God to cause the shadow of the sun to go backward on the sun dial, like He did for King Hezekiah, to give me more time, but He has chosen not to do so. I have resigned myself that this body can no longer do what my mind wants it to do. I have come to peace with that – and with God.

"The midwife tells me there is nothing more that can be done, so I have decided to enjoy whatever time I have left with my family around me. And here you are! Now tell me about your life in Jerusalem!"

Tali and I told him about our many new experiences in the city, but we had already decided not to burden him with the prejudices we had encountered from some of his distant relatives. He expressed his pride that I was now one of the most powerful men in the entire region.

Ishmael already knew how I felt about the role, so he smiled faintly as I said, "I am first and foremost a servant of the Almighty God, placed in this role by His divine hand. Any power I have is His, by His grace and for His purpose. I am grateful to serve Him wherever He places me."

After we had visited for a while, we told him to get some rest and we would talk more later. Within moments he was fast asleep, and we made our way out of his bed chamber to the central part of the house. Salome and her sons, James and John, had just arrived.

Salome's older son, James, continued to work as a fisherman with his father. Zebedee had sent his wife and son to see Ishmael, but had stayed behind to tend to their fishing business. As he often reminded us, if he didn't catch any fish, he didn't make any money. What's more, our family would have less fish to process and sell through our warehouse. He seldom failed to tell us he was keeping all of us fed! Salome assured us Zebedee would come see Ishmael as soon as he could.

Her son John had also been one of the fishermen on the boats until he left Bethsaida to seek out John the baptizer. Zebedee had graciously released his son to go because he knew his son had a special calling from God. That's why he had also allowed John to study with me in Capernaum and continue his training in the Scriptures at the feet of Gamaliel in Jerusalem. Though John had been born a fisherman, Zebedee knew his God-given passions lie elsewhere.

In recent days, the Sanhedrin had spent a great deal of time discussing the baptizer. Annas and others were expressing great concern about his growing popularity. After the death of his parents, the baptizer had been raised by his uncle, who was an Essene. Annas knew the Essenes held little regard for the Pharisees and even less for the Sadducees. So Annas and the others were convinced the baptizer's teachings would undermine the authority of the Sanhedrin.

He convinced Caiaphas to send a delegation of priests and scribes to question the baptizer. But, knowing the baptizer was being held in such high regard by the people, Annas also instructed them to be baptized by John so the people would believe his teaching was under the authority of the Sanhedrin. Though I knew I could not agree with another one of Annas's schemes, I also knew I needed to learn more about John the baptizer.

Now was my opportunity! Later in the day, I drew my nephew John aside so we could talk about his time with the baptizer.

∼

14

WHO IS THIS BAPTIZER?

~

"There is no question John is the one God sent to prepare the way for the Messiah," my nephew told me. "The Spirit of God rests mightily upon him. Though he rightly proclaims the truth of God, he is not an eloquent speaker. The people are not being drawn to him by his gift of oratory, they are being drawn by God's Spirit.

"As one of his disciples, I can tell you he is not looking for fortune or fame. His clothing is simple, his diet is modest, and he sleeps in a cave or under the open sky. He seeks no money from anyone. All he seeks is that people repent of their sins and turn their hearts toward Jehovah God and the One who is coming.

"I have grown up around religious leaders. Some, like you, have a servant's heart. But most have become corrupted by the power and wealth of their position. John is not anything like them! He seeks to serve God with all that he is. The religious leaders need not fear that he seeks to take their power; rather, he prays that we might all turn from our sinful ways and return to the only One who has all authority and power."

"What happened when the most recent delegation from the Sanhedrin arrived to question the baptizer?" I asked.

"They asked him if he claimed to be the Messiah!" John responded. "Anyone who has listened to the baptizer for more than five minutes knows that he makes no such claim. It was a foolish question he flatly denied. So then they asked, '*Well then, are you Elijah returned from God?*'[1]

"When he told them no, they asked, '*Then who are you? Tell us so we can give an answer to those who sent us. What do you have to say about yourself?*'[2]

"The baptizer replied, quoting the prophet Isaiah, '*I am a voice shouting in the wilderness. Prepare a straight pathway for the Lord's coming!*'"[3]

"The Pharisees and Sadducees responded, 'Then baptize us so we might be prepared for the Lord's coming.'

"But the baptizer knew what was in their hearts when he exclaimed, '*You brood of snakes! Who warned you to flee God's coming judgment? Prove by the way you live that you have truly turned from your sins and turned to God. I baptize with water those who turn from their sins and turn to God. But Someone is coming soon who is far greater than I am – and He will clean up the threshing floor, storing the grain in His barn and burning the chaff with never-ending fire!*'"[4]

"The baptizer made no secret as to who the chaff was. The religious leaders turned in a huff and walked away with haste!"

"They may have walked away for now," I interjected, "but I am certain they will return. They fear him too much to ignore him."

"I understand, uncle," John replied, "but the One they should really fear is the One who is coming soon – the One who will clean up the threshing floor."

I nodded my head in agreement. "Yes, they should! But I fear their hearts will be too hard to receive even Him!"

Just then the midwife entered the room and told us Ishmael had taken his last breath. "Jehovah God has allowed him to die peacefully in his sleep," she said.

I pronounced a traditional word of blessing over his body. "Blessed are You, Oh Lord our God, King of the universe, the Just God. You are the Giver of life. The very breath that we breathe comes from You. We thank You for the time You have given us with Ishmael. Blessed be Your name."

We then prepared his body for burial and carried him in procession to the tomb before the sun set. Tali and I remained in Capernaum for the next seven days for a period of grief and mourning. The people of Capernaum showered our family with love and affection – which made it even harder for us to leave one week later. But we knew it was time for me to return to my duties in Jerusalem.

As we made the journey back, I had a lot of time to think about my conversation with John about the baptizer – and about the One whose coming He said was soon. We had looked forward to His coming for generations. Each generation had prayed He would come in their lifetime. Could now truly be the time?

My thoughts drifted to Annas and Caiaphas and the men who were a part of their inner circle. How would they receive this news? For that matter, how would any of us in the Sanhedrin receive the news? Would we welcome Him with open arms – or would some members plot against Him like they were doing against the baptizer?

And what about me? Would I be a part of the grain or the chaff? Something told me we wouldn't have long to wait and see!

15

REPORTS ABOUT A GALILEAN CARPENTER

~

hen Tali and I arrived back in Jerusalem, the members of the Sanhedrin were in an uproar. As expected, they were up in arms about the baptizer. Most of them were arguing that he needed to be brought to Jerusalem for questioning before the full council. As I walked into the great hall, Annas's son, Eleazar, was already speaking.

"This wild man must learn his radical teaching will not be tolerated by this council," he bellowed. "We cannot have him dividing our people. He disrespected those we sent to question him, which essentially was disrespecting this entire body and the authority granted to us by Jehovah God.

"The people are watching to see what we will do. If we do nothing, people will think he is in the right and we are weak! We must take swift action! Send a contingent of the temple guards to arrest him and bring him before us."

Gamaliel was the first to respond. "Eleazar, if we do that, the people will rebel against us. The people are beginning to flock to him to be baptized.

They believe he speaks with the authority of the prophets. If we arrest him, we will look like the evil kings who persecuted the prophets.

"What part of his message do you think we should discredit? Should we tell the people they should not repent? Should we deny the prophecies of a coming Messiah? Or perhaps you believe we should tell them not to be baptized?

"How hypocritical! Do we not, ourselves, tell the people they need to repent and present sacrifices? Do we not also teach about the coming Messiah in our synagogues? Are there not over 700 mikvah pools surrounding this temple where we tell the people to purify themselves in water before walking through these gates?"

Caiaphas raised his hand to preclude anyone else from speaking. When the hall was silent, he said, "Gamaliel again speaks wisdom to us. If we take any action right now, it will only enhance the baptizer's influence over the people. We must find a way to affirm his message of repentance while correcting him for his youthful impetuousness in disrespecting those of us in authority. Let's continue to watch and see what he does while we wait for the right opportunity.

"Besides, we have an even greater concern before us. I have just received news the Roman emperor is sending a new prefect (regional governor) to replace Valerius Gratus. Though I will not personally miss him when he is gone, we have at least been able to come to an understanding with him.

"Do not forget that when he first assumed his office, he demanded a new high priest be placed in office every year. He did so to keep us off balance. And as you recall, his plan worked!"

Annas interrupted. "Until I was able to convince him of the wisdom of continuity of leadership, and he wisely selected you, Caiaphas, to assume the role."

"That is true, Annas," Caiaphas acknowledged. "And since then, thanks to you and the others who stood with you, we have been able to function with some degree of mutual tolerance. But now, with his departure, we have a new prefect who is unfamiliar to us. How will he view us? Will he seek to disband us or strip us of some of our authority over civil affairs?"

"What do we know about him, Caiaphas?" Annas asked.

"Very little," Caiaphas replied. "His name is Pontius Pilate. He is a distinguished cavalry officer and the grandson of an influential leader in the Roman senate. He has caught the eye of Emperor Tiberius and been rewarded with this position. But he knows nothing about us, our history, or our beliefs. He is a pagan like all the rest of them and has the potential to cause more trouble than good."

Annas spoke up again, but this time he was clearly addressing all the members. "That of course is true, Caiaphas. But we still have friends in Rome – alliances that we have built over many years. Tiberius does not want trouble here in Judea. He wants us to pay our taxes, and he wants to maintain the peace. He is content to leave us alone if both of those things continue."

Then he added with a smile, "I doubt Pontius Pilate will want to upset that proverbial apple cart. Let us watch and see. If the need arises for us to convince him to go along with us, I'm sure we will find a way."

Sensing it was time to move on to another topic, Theophilus addressed the high priest. "Caiaphas, I have another matter we need to discuss."

"What is it, Theophilus?" Caiaphas asked.

"I am hearing reports of a Galilean carpenter who is beginning to make a name for Himself up in that region," Theophilus answered. "It is said He is a miracle worker. He apparently amazed a large group at a wedding feast in Cana by turning six washing pots of water into wine. And the guests reported it was the best wine they had ever tasted.

"Then, after He was done teaching from a boat on the sea, He instructed the fishermen to cast their nets in a place that shortly before had yielded no fish. But at His word, they cast their nets and their boats nearly sank from the quantity of fish. Word of these deeds – and others – is beginning to spread, and He is starting to gather a following."

∾

16

A SURPRISE IN THE TEMPLE

～

*A*nnas quickly interjected. "It sounds like He is worthy of watching, Theophilus. Anyone who can provide great quantities of fish and good-tasting wine will always be welcome at my table!"

Annas began to laugh heartily as others quickly joined in. Then he turned to me and said with a smirk, "Nicodemus, what about you? What do you know about your fellow Galilean? Is He a carpenter, a fish monger, or a vintner? Should we afford Him any more attention than we would give to any other Galilean? Perhaps you are the best equipped to investigate this miracle worker and give us a report. After all, you have much in common!"

Caiaphas interrupted before I could respond. "Annas, enough of your sarcastic goading about Galilee. Perhaps I should give Nicodemus the floor to tell us what Galileans think of Judeans. But then again, he is far too much of a gentleman to do that. Let us turn our attention to more important matters!"

As the weeks passed, I continued to hear reports about this carpenter named Jesus of Nazareth. With Passover now approaching, I wondered if I might see Him here in Jerusalem. But with so many pilgrims coming to the city, how could I possibly hope to recognize Him?

The day the Passover celebration began was no different from any other year. People came from all over to bring their offerings to the Lord. Those who traveled from afar usually purchased their offerings of animals or birds from the merchants in the temple. King Solomon had implemented the practice many years ago.

But in recent years, while Annas was high priest, the merchant tables and stalls had been moved into the outer courtyard of the temple instead of the stoa outside the walls as King Solomon had decreed. We were told the move was needed because of increased demand. But truth be told, it had become a lucrative enterprise for the temple treasury – and for those who oversaw it.

The temple priests were instructed to reject any offering that had even the slightest blemish. This meant the pilgrim must forgo presenting an offering or find an acceptable substitute. Since the whole purpose for coming to the temple was to present an offering, the merchants were only too happy to help the pilgrim rectify the dilemma.

The whole process had evolved gradually over time, and no one gave much thought to the significant financial gains being pocketed by some of our leaders. It was meeting a need, so it became an accepted practice.

That is … until the day Jesus arrived at the temple.

Our council was meeting when we heard shouts and screams coming from the outer courtyard. We hastily went to see what all the commotion was about.

Chaos was everywhere. The moneychangers' tables had been overturned, and the merchants were feverishly gathering their coins from the ground. Portions of the animal stalls were lying in pieces on the ground, and men were hurriedly driving the oxen, cattle, and sheep out through the gate.

Several of the bird cages had careened onto the ground and the doves were taking flight. In the center of it all was one Man. He had a whip made of rope in His hand and He was chasing all the merchants out of the temple. The pilgrims stood there watching in amazement. No one had ever witnessed such a sight – particularly in the temple.

Even amid all the noise, I could hear the Man shouting, *"Get these things out of here! Don't turn My Father's house into a marketplace!"*[1]

Who was this Man? And who had given Him the authority to do what He was doing? He kept referring to the temple as His Father's house. Of course, it is our Father God's house, but He was saying those words in a much more personal way.

And His anger was not uncontrolled emotion. This Man was very much in control. At that moment, I was full of remorse. I realized He was doing something we all should have done – a long time ago. We had desecrated the temple by permitting this merchants' fair to take place in it. We had sinned. And only this Man had the presence of mind and courage to confront it for what it was. Only this Man was willing to stand up on His own and confront the sin.

Though I didn't know who He was, I stood ashamed before Him. I looked up and saw Annas and Caiaphas watching from a corner of the courtyard. They were obviously seething – but neither said anything. I looked around and saw several of my Sanhedrin brothers who were obviously conflicted over what was happening. But no one dared to move. I saw shame in the eyes of Joseph of Arimathea, who was now standing beside me. "Who is this Man?" I asked him.

"He is Jesus of Nazareth – the carpenter from Galilee!" Joseph replied.

17

WHO GAVE HIM THE AUTHORITY?

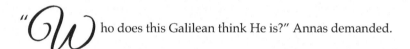

"W ho does this Galilean think He is?" Annas demanded.

We were all back in the great hall. The crowd in the temple courtyard had dispersed, but not before Annas and Caiaphas had decided to confront Jesus over His actions.

"What right do You have to do these things?"[1] Annas asked Him.

Jesus had looked at them with a piercing gaze but did not answer. That seemed to enrage Annas even more.

"If God has given You the authority to do this, show us a miraculous sign to prove it!"[2] Annas shouted.

Jesus's demeanor was a sharp contrast to the men who stood before Him. The anger He had displayed a few moments before was much different from what I saw in Annas's eyes. Jesus stood before them calmly and in control. He was not intimidated by these high priests. He responded to them deliberately and firmly. *"All right. Destroy this temple, and in three days I will raise it up."*[3]

Even I was startled by His answer.

"What!" Annas shouted. "It took forty-six years to build this temple, and You can do it in three days?"[4]

But again, Jesus remained silent. He had given His answer. He obviously saw no need to repeat it or justify it. Instead, He walked on into the temple and left Annas and Caiaphas to stare after Him incredulously.

As I watched this unfold, a prophecy from the Scriptures came to my mind: *"Passion for God's house burns within Me."*[5] And I thought – who is this Jesus?

The great hall was abuzz. Many were taking the same position as Annas. This council, led by the high priest, was given the authority under God to direct what could and could not take place inside these walls. Who was this Man to question their authority?

But slowly the conversation began to turn. It was Joseph of Arimathea who was the first to bravely speak up. "But He is right! There was a reason our ancestors kept that activity outside the temple. By bringing it inside, we have turned the courtyard from a place where those entering the temple should be preparing their hearts for prayer and worship into a huckster's market. I, for one, was ashamed that He needed to correct us. In our hearts, we knew it was wrong – or at least we should have – but we did nothing!"

Annas raised his voice to object, but to my surprise his voice was drowned out by a number of voices agreeing with Joseph. Annas watched in amazement as the tide in the room turned against him. Probably for the first time, he sensed he had lost control of the discussion. He did not have the support of the majority.

Seeing what was taking place, Caiaphas intervened. "These are both valid concerns! Annas asks an appropriate question about this Man called Jesus. But Joseph also raises a valid concern. The two matters need not be connected to one another. We will defer further discussion until we have had adequate opportunity to investigate both matters. Until then, the stalls and stables will remain outside in the stoa. As in all things, we will reconsider these matters only after we have had time to pray and fast."

Annas obviously did not like Caiaphas's answer, but he nodded his head in deference to his son-in-law. I was certain there would be much conversation later that night around the family dinner table – but until then we would move on.

As I left later that afternoon, I saw a large crowd surrounding Jesus. Many who were sick were being brought to Him for healing. I personally saw those who had been lame now walking. I saw vision restored to a blind man. And I saw deaf men who could now hear.

Each day throughout the remainder of Passover, the crowds around Jesus increased. He was teaching them from the Scriptures with an authority that surpassed that of great teachers like Gamaliel. I had never witnessed anyone like Him, and I knew I needed to know more about Him. Also, as a member of the Sanhedrin, I needed to be certain this Man was not leading our people astray.

I doubted Caiaphas would select me as one of the members assigned to formally investigate Jesus, but I still felt the need to do so on my own. He was from Galilee, after all. I wasn't sure how I would go about accomplishing this – until I saw my nephew John standing beside Jesus.

～

18

I WANT TO SEE FOR MYSELF

~

I walked over to John and asked, "How is it that you are here in the temple with Jesus of Nazareth?"

"Greetings, Uncle!" John replied. "You look surprised to see me! I have come to Jerusalem to celebrate Passover with the Master."

"The Master?" I asked. "Why do you call Jesus the Master? When we were last together you were a disciple of the baptizer. Is he here in Jerusalem, as well?"

"No, the baptizer is not here," John answered. "He continues to preach his message of repentance and baptize those who respond in the Jordan River. I am now a disciple of Jesus."

I couldn't contain my surprise as I asked, "How has that come to be?"

"One afternoon several weeks ago," John began, "my friend Andrew and I were standing beside the baptizer when he told us, '*Look! There is the Lamb of God!*'[(1)] He was pointing at Jesus. You can imagine our confusion. So, we asked him what he meant.

"He told us, 'Six weeks ago, this Man came to me and asked me to baptize Him. At first, I didn't know who He was. I should have recognized Him. I actually saw Him a few times when we were both boys. I am told we first met when we were both in our mothers' wombs. You see, our mothers were cousins.' But the baptizer's mother had died long ago, so their families hadn't seen one another since.

"Then he continued, 'When God told me to begin my ministry several years ago, He told me that one day I would see the Holy Spirit descend and rest upon Someone when I baptized Him. God told me He would be the One I was looking for – the very Son of God! That happened when I baptized Jesus that day. And I heard a voice from heaven confirm it by saying, "*You are My Beloved Son, and I am fully pleased with You.*"'[(2)]

"As soon as Andrew and I heard the baptizer's words and saw Jesus, we knew He was the One we were to follow. The two of us, together with another one of the baptizer's disciples who was standing with us, immediately turned and followed Jesus.

"We never looked back. From that moment, I have continued to follow Jesus. I was with Him at a wedding feast several weeks ago when He turned water into wine. I was one of the fishermen in a boat when He directed us to cast our nets, only to draw in the largest catch of fish anyone has ever seen!"

These were the stories Theophilus had reported to the Sanhedrin a few weeks ago. And now my nephew was confirming he had been there, and these things were true!

John continued. "Since then, I have witnessed Him heal the sick and make the lame to walk, the deaf to hear, and the blind to see! And what's more,

He speaks the words of heaven with an authority I have never heard – and as you know, I have been taught by some tremendous teachers. But Jesus's knowledge and authority exceeds each one, including you, Uncle. Jesus is without a doubt the Son of God!"

I interrupted him saying, "John, that is quite a declaration to make! If it is true, all our people have cause to rejoice! But we must know it is true – without any reservation!"

"Uncle, He is in the temple each day teaching the people," John offered. "Come join them, listen to Him, and know for yourself. Everyone is welcome at His feet when they come as honest seekers. Come, let me introduce you."

"I can't come to Him right now," I answered, "or any other time here in the temple. After what He did a few days ago – when He drove out the merchants – many of my Sanhedrin brothers do not trust Him. If I were to be seen in public speaking with Him, those same men would no longer trust me. I must speak with Him in private. Are you able to arrange a time and place for us to meet?"

"Yes, I believe I can," John replied. "Do you know the shop of Yitzhak the weaver here in the city?"

"Yes, I do."

"He has a room over his shop," John added. "Come to that room two nights from now after the dinner hour when the city has become quiet."

"Can you assure me no one else will know about our meeting?" I asked.

"Only Jesus and I will know," John answered. "I will be there to introduce you."

For the next two days I thought about little else other than my upcoming meeting with Jesus. I told no one other than Tali about my plan, including my friend Joseph of Arimathea. I needed to know for certain who Jesus was before I could admit to seeking Him out. I knew other members of the Sanhedrin had been sent to question Him – but they were trying to discredit Him. I wanted to speak to Him so I would know for certain if He is the Son of God.

I knew I was risking my position in the Sanhedrin and in the community. I truly believed there were some in the Sanhedrin who would never look on Jesus favorably – even if it was proven beyond question that He is the Son of God. As a matter of fact, they would see Him – and anyone who associates with Him – as an even greater enemy.

19

"YOU MUST BE BORN AGAIN!"

~

I was very familiar with the shop of Yitzhak the weaver. Tali had purchased all the fabric she used to decorate and furnish our home from Yitzhak. He was a well-known and respected merchant in the city.

He was working at his bench when I arrived. I decided to greet him before quietly making my way up the stairway to meet Jesus.

"Welcome to my shop, Rabbi Nicodemus!" he exclaimed. "What brings you here at such a late hour?"

Not wanting to tell him the real reason for my visit, I replied, "I was walking by and saw the lights in your window. I could see you were busy at work, but I decided to stop and extend my greeting."

"I am so glad you did," Yitzhak responded. "How are your wife and your family?"

"My wife is well and very pleased with the fine fabrics you sold us," I answered. "It has been some time since we have heard from our children, but we know Jehovah God is watching over them. And how are your wife and family?"

I had no idea how his answer would better prepare me for my conversation with Jesus. "We, too, know Jehovah God is watching over us!" Yitzhak told me. "Earlier this week, my son, Uriah, was helping me finish the construction of our upper room. We were setting the final roof tiles when he lost his footing and fell to the street below. I scurried down as fast as I could.

"I felt so helpless as I stared at him lying there lifeless. All I could do was cry out to Jehovah God to help me. Just as I did, a Man knelt beside me. He appeared to be just one of the many pilgrims who had traveled to Jerusalem for Passover.

"The next thing I knew He took my son by the hand and said, 'Young man, I say to you, arise!' Immediately, my son sat up. Uriah looked at me, then he looked at the Stranger. The Stranger returned my son's look and said, 'Young man, behold your father.' Then He looked at me and said, 'Father, behold your son!'

"It was as if my son had never fallen. Just a moment before he had been lying there lifeless on the street! I was bewildered. I looked up at the Man and asked, 'Who are You? And what have You done?'

"'Yitzhak,' He said, 'you cried out to the Father for help. He heard your prayer, and your son has been made whole. All so the Father might be glorified.'"

I couldn't contain my joy over God's miraculous intervention. "Praise be to Jehovah God our Protector!" I exclaimed. "Yitzhak, I praise the Lord with you!! Who was the Man?"

"His name is Jesus of Nazareth!" he replied.

For the previous two days, I had asked Jehovah God to show me clearly through this meeting that Jesus was His Son. And now, Jehovah God had shown me even before I had spoken a word to Jesus.

After a short while, I bid Yitzhak a good night and made my way up the stairway to the upper room without being seen. When I entered, only Jesus and John were present.

After my nephew introduced me to Jesus, I asked, *"Rabbi, we all know that God has sent You to teach us. Your miraculous signs are evidence that God is with You."* [1]

Jesus wasted no time with shallow compliments. Instead, He moved right to the heart of the matter as He replied, *"I tell you the truth, unless you are born again, you cannot see the Kingdom of God."* [2]

I didn't understand what He meant, so I asked, *"What do You mean? How can an old man go back into his mother's womb and be born again?"* [3]

Jesus replied, *"Nicodemus, I assure you, no one can enter the Kingdom of God without being born of water and the Spirit. Humans can reproduce only human life, but the Holy Spirit gives birth to spiritual life."* [4]

I still didn't understand. *"How are these things possible?"* [5] I asked.

I felt like I was a talmid sitting at the feet of my Teacher as Jesus answered. *"You are a respected Jewish teacher, and yet you don't understand these things? I tell you what I know and have seen, and yet you won't believe My testimony. But if you don't believe Me when I tell you about earthly things, how can you possibly believe if I tell you about heavenly things? No one has ever gone to heaven and returned. But the Son of Man has come down from heaven. And as Moses lifted up the bronze snake on a pole in the wilderness, so the Son of Man must be lifted up, so that everyone who believes in Him will have eternal life.*[6]

"For this is how God loved the world: He gave His one and only Son, so that everyone who believes in Him will not perish but have eternal life. God sent His Son to save the world through Him.[7]

"There is no judgment against anyone who believes in Him. But anyone who does not believe in Him has already been judged for not believing in God's one and only Son. And the judgment is based on this fact: God's light came into the world, but people loved the darkness more than the light, for their actions were evil. All who do evil hate the light and refuse to go near it for fear their sins will be exposed. But those who do what is right come to the light so others can see that they are doing what God wants."[8]

෴

20

WHAT DO I DO NOW?

~

*A*s I made my way home, I pondered what Jesus had said. But His last statement in particular kept echoing in my mind: *"Those who do what is right come to the light so others can see that they are doing what God wants."*[1]

I wanted to do right. That's why I had come to talk to Jesus that night. I wanted to do what God wants me to do. I always have. But I knew something had been missing in my life. Was obeying the law of Moses not enough? And who was able to always obey the law? Try as I might, I knew I couldn't.

Jesus had said only those who believe in God's Son will have eternal life and that God had sent His Son to save the world through Him. Is that what was missing in my life? Must I believe in God's Son? And if so, is Jesus truly God's Son as He says? My nephew, John, believes He is. But do I?

As I asked myself that question over and over again, I began to realize I *did* believe Jesus is the Son of God! And if I were to be completely honest, I had known it when I was standing before Him that night. For that matter, I had known it the day I had seen Him drive the merchants out of the temple.

No longer would I deny that reality, which meant I must also acknowledge that everything Jesus said to me was true! He was the promised One. He was the One God sent to deliver His people from their sins. So, what was I to do now? Do I leave the Sanhedrin to follow Jesus as John has done? Or do I follow Jesus from within the Sanhedrin? Does God want me to be light from within the council?

When I arrived home, I told Tali about my time with Jesus. I conveyed everything He had said and all that I had considered as I walked home. I told her I believed Jesus to be the Son of God.

When I finished, she looked at me and said, "I have been praying God would reveal Himself to you through your time with Jesus. The Spirit of God reminded me earlier tonight of the words written by the prophet Jeremiah: '*If you look for Me wholeheartedly, you will find Me.*'[(2)] Nicodemus, I know you are a man who has sought God wholeheartedly. Tonight, He has enabled you to find Him! Give all praise to Jehovah God – and trust what His Spirit is saying to you."

"I do trust Him," I said, "and I know what Jesus told me is true. Now I need to know what He would have me do with this truth."

Tali took me by the hand and said, "Then we will ask Him to show you and trust Him to do so."

It was late when I went to bed, and my mind continued to replay my time with Jesus. I kept hearing Him say, "*so others can see. ...*" By the time the sun rose, I knew what I must do.

God had placed me in the high council; not by chance, but according to His plan. I was to shine His light in the midst of the great darkness within the Sanhedrin. It would not be well received. But His Spirit reminded me I was not responsible for the results – I was responsible to shine the light.

The Spirit prompted me to speak with Joseph of Arimathea first. He listened intently with an open mind and an open heart. When I finished, he thanked me and told me what I shared was helpful, but he was not ready to believe Jesus is the Son of God.

After that conversation, I realized each of us needs to have a personal encounter with Jesus. We cannot convince others of who Jesus is – that's the work of the Spirit of God. My responsibility was to be light pointing others to Jesus. So that's what I set about doing in the days and weeks that followed.

Joseph came to me several weeks later. He had been asked to accompany Annas and Caiaphas on a journey to Arimathea to question Ashriel, the local rabbi. He was the great-grandson of a priest named Simeon who, in his old age, had supposedly seen a baby he believed to be the promised Messiah. Rabbi Ashriel was said to have been with his great-grandfather that day.

Joseph had agreed to make the journey if Gamaliel and I accompanied them, too. He wanted unbiased witnesses to the conversation. Annas and Caiaphas had agreed, so he was asking me to go along. I did not hesitate for a moment!

Given the number of years that had passed since that event, the baby would now be a man of about thirty years of age. My heart raced as we made the journey to Arimathea.

～

21

A JOURNEY TO ARIMATHEA

~

*W*hen we arrived at the home of Ashriel in Arimathea, Caiaphas told us Annas would lead the conversation. Ashriel looked at our group warily until he spotted Joseph. His face lit up as he exclaimed, "Joseph, it is good to see you! We miss seeing you and your family at the synagogue!"

The two men embraced as Joseph replied, "And we miss all of you, as well! We look forward to the day we can rejoin you here in Arimathea."

To the consternation of Annas, Joseph went on to explain why we were there. Ashriel clearly trusted him, so Joseph was able to set his mind at ease. After the two men exchanged updates about their families, Joseph relinquished the conversation to Annas, who asked, "Why did Simeon believe the baby he saw was the Messiah?"

We all listened intently as Ashriel relayed the story. "My great-grandfather never doubted that day would come. Even though it had been almost one hundred years since God had given him the promise he would see the

Messiah before he died, his faith was as strong that day as it had been on the day God first spoke to him.

"That morning, when he saw the baby and His parents, he just knew! He told me to help him walk over to the baby. His step grew quicker and steadier, and he told me his heart was pounding in his chest. When we arrived at the family, Papa asked if he could see the baby. I'm sure his actions seemed strange to them, but they kindly turned their young son so Papa could look into His eyes.

"Tears began to stream down his cheeks! I'll never forget his words when he turned to the baby's mother. 'This Child of yours will cause many people in Israel to fall and others to stand. The Child will be like a warning sign. Many people will reject Him, and you, young mother, will suffer as though you had been stabbed by a dagger. But all this will show what is really in the hearts of people.'[(1)]

"She didn't speak a word but simply nodded at my great-grandpa. I was struck by her tenderness. I could see why Jehovah God had chosen her to be the mother of His Son. When Papa reached to pick up the baby, she willingly handed the tiny bundle to him.

"The baby didn't stir or make a sound as Papa held Him. Rather, the baby seemed to look intently into my great-grandpa's eyes. It was as if the baby knew him. And I became convinced the baby *did* know him.

"As Papa held Him in his arms, he looked toward heaven and said, '*Lord, I am Your servant, and now I can die in peace, because You have kept Your promise to me. With my own eyes I have seen what You have done to save Your people.*'[(2)]

"Papa returned the baby to His mother's arms and blessed her and the father. We watched as they walked away. Papa turned to me and said, 'These people have no idea they have been in the presence of the Son of God,' as he pointed to those moving about the temple.

"Papa died not long after that. But he did so knowing his lifelong mission was complete."

Annas asked the question that was on all of our minds. "Did they tell you the baby's name or where they were from?"

"No," he replied, "they did not, and we never asked."

As Annas continued to ask questions, I found myself believing Jesus was indeed that baby. I think the other men did, too – or at least thought it was possible – but no one said it out loud. I thought about what Simeon had said to the baby's mother, "He will show what is really in the hearts of people." And I knew that was true!

During the years that followed, Caiaphas and Annas frequently brought up the subject of Jesus before the Sanhedrin. They repeatedly raised false accusations. "He is Beelzebub!" "He is a demon." "He is a false witness." "He is a fraud." Occasionally they would say things that were closer to what they truly believed. "He is leading the people away from us. He is usurping our authority. We are in danger of losing our power."

Both men became obsessed with defeating Jesus. This went far beyond their embarrassment the day He cleansed the temple. These men feared Him, and they knew if they didn't discredit Him soon, it would be too late. But they didn't want to just discredit Him – they wanted to destroy Him.

For months they sent messengers trying to entrap Jesus into saying something they could use against Him. But every time, Jesus responded in a way that revealed their treachery.

As time passed, I began to openly ask the question in council meetings as to whether Jesus might be the Promised One. One day, as I looked around the room at each man, I asked, "Have we allowed our fear of losing our power and positions to blind us from seeing the very One we have waited for so many years? Instead of plotting against Him, should we not be welcoming Him into our midst?"

The silence that followed was deafening!

22

TWO MIRACLES IN CAPERNAUM

❦

*S*oon after Tali and I moved to Jerusalem, Jesus's mother, Mary, had moved to Capernaum. Several of the young men from our village – my nephews, James and John; as well as our former tax collector, Matthew – were now numbered among His disciples. My sister-in-law, Salome, was also traveling with Jesus. As a result, He visited Capernaum often to see His mother and permit His followers to spend time with their families.

Whenever Jairus, Leah, and our granddaughter, Ilana, came to Jerusalem to celebrate the feasts and visit with us, they would captivate us with stories of what Jesus had said or done on His last visit to the village. But we were completely amazed by one particular event Jairus relayed to us. "A few weeks ago, a royal procession arrived in Capernaum. It was King Herod's chamberlain, Chuza, and his wife, Joanna. I soon learned their ten-year-old son, Samuel, was ill with a high fever, and they had come seeking Jesus.

"Mary told them He was expected any day. The last she had heard He and His followers were in Samaria near Sychar. They would be returning by way of Cana. Chuza decided to leave his wife and son in the village and go out alone to meet up with Jesus. I promised to look in on the boy until Chuza returned.

"I was there the next day. It was a little after the noon hour and there was still no sign of Chuza – or more importantly, Jesus. We had all heard about the power Jesus had to heal those who were sick, but I feared the boy would soon die. I believed Jesus was going to be too late to save him. I couldn't imagine the grief these parents would experience. Just then, I heard Samuel gasp as he crossed what I feared was the threshold into death.

"But suddenly, the boy began to stir. He sat up in bed as if nothing was wrong. I quickly realized his fever was gone! I looked around the room to see if Jesus had entered without my knowing – but He was not there. It was about one o'clock in the afternoon.

"It was the next day before we learned from Chuza that Jesus had simply spoken the words there in Cana, *'Go back to your son. He will live!'*[1] He had spoken those words at the exact moment I heard Samuel gasp. Jesus had spoken, and a boy who was miles away had been healed!"

Jairus confessed that he and Leah both believed in Jesus that day. By the grace of Jehovah God, He was permitting our entire family to come to know and believe in His Son.

Several months later, Jairus and his family returned to celebrate the Festival of Lights with us – and the story they told us this time was much closer to home! "Two weeks ago," Jairus began, "Ilana started to run a high fever. It was the same fever we had all witnessed in many others. Most of those people had died – except Samuel, the boy Jesus had healed.

"Jesus had been in the village the day before Ilana got sick, but then He and his disciples had departed by boat and crossed over the sea. Many of His followers had remained in Capernaum, though, so I knew He would be returning soon. I continued to keep watch for Him. I knew He could heal Ilana!

"Before long I began hearing a commotion in the street. I heard people shouting, 'Jesus is back! They are about to arrive on the shore!' I ran as fast as I could and got there just as He was stepping out of the boat. I fell at His feet and pleaded with Him – '*My little daughter is dying. Please come, lay Your hands on her and heal her so she can live.*'[(2)]

"Without saying a word, Jesus reached down, helped me to my feet, and the two of us began to make our way toward the village. Our progress, however, was slowed by the crowd pressing in on Jesus from all sides. As we were making our way, messengers arrived to tell me Ilana had died. '*There's no use troubling the Teacher now.*'[(3)] It was too late!

"But Jesus overheard the messengers, took me by the arm, and said, '*Don't be afraid. Just have faith.*'[(4)] Then He stopped the crowd and told them to remain on the shore.

"When we arrived at our home, Jesus saw the weeping and wailing of the people who had gathered to mourn. As we walked by, Jesus asked, '*Why all this commotion and weeping? The child isn't dead; she's only asleep.*'[(5)]

"The people in my house looked at one another and then started to laugh at Jesus. I knew many in the crowd had not seen Him perform miracles like I had – but they had heard of His miracles!

"As Jesus looked at them, their laughter stopped and turned into an uncomfortable silence. Because of their faithlessness, He told them all to leave my home. Afterward, Jesus walked with Leah and me into the room where Ilana was lying. Then He took her hand in His and said, '*Little girl, get up!*'[(6)]

"Immediately, she sat up! Just like Samuel had! It was as if she had never been sick. Ilana stood and began to walk around!"

I looked over at my precious granddaughter as tears of joy streamed down my cheeks. Tali and I both wrapped our arms around Ilana as we praised God for His goodness and mercy to us. We were overcome with a feeling of indebtedness to the One who had brought our granddaughter back to life! Jesus was already our Savior – but after we heard what He had done, He became our Lord and Master. Some have foolishly said Ilana wasn't really dead, she was only asleep. I, however, would suggest they talk to us – her family – or any of those who mistakenly chose to laugh at Jesus.

23

A LINE IN THE SAND

~

*a*s time passed, Sanhedrin members became even more fearful that Jesus was undermining their authority. More than once, He had refused to submit to their rule. They were afraid the people would do likewise to the point the Sanhedrin would be stripped of their power and their positions would become irrelevant.

But Annas, Caiaphas, and the others no longer openly plotted against Jesus; they knew some of us would not support their plans. Instead of discussing their schemes in front of the entire council, they held hushed conversations in the hallways or at the high priest's private residence.

This past October, Jesus was back in Jerusalem for the observance of the Feast of Tabernacles. As expected, throngs of people flocked to Him as He taught and healed in the courtyard. It was obvious that certain members of the council did not like it!

One morning we were gathered in the hall hearing a petition forwarded to us by the local Sanhedrin in Jericho. It was a civil dispute between two citizens in the city.

During our deliberation, two priests entered the hall followed by four temple guards. Two of the guards were grasping the arms of a disheveled woman. A collective gasp arose from the council. Women were not permitted in the council hall, and this woman was certainly not dressed appropriately for any venue, let alone the temple or the Hall of Hewn Stones.

The two priests quickly approached Caiaphas. I recognized one of them. I had seen him speaking with Caiaphas on several previous occasions.

The priests spoke with Caiaphas and Annas in hushed tones. Soon a smile crossed Annas's lips. I couldn't imagine why he was smiling. Nothing about this situation merited a smile. After a few moments, Caiaphas turned to the guards and ordered them to take the woman into the court-yard where Jesus was teaching.

Caiaphas then instructed several members of the Sanhedrin to accompany the priests into the courtyard. I knew these men were some of his key allies in plotting against Jesus, so I feared what was about to take place. I got up and followed them out so I could witness whatever happened.

The crowd in the courtyard began to stir as soon as they saw the woman. Jesus stopped speaking. All eyes turned toward the woman. I noticed that both priests, as well as those sent by Caiaphas, were each picking up a stone. They were obviously preparing to stone the woman. Suddenly everything became quiet. One of the priests, who had spoken with Caiaphas, addressed Jesus. *"Teacher, this woman was caught in the act of adultery. The law of Moses says to stone her. What do You say?"*[1]

Jesus looked at the woman, who bowed her head in fear and shame. In contrast, her accusers stood scowling at her with looks of contempt. Surrounding them was the crowd – leering at her and craning their necks to see what Jesus was going to say. He was the only One who didn't look at her with condemnation.

After a few moments, He stooped down and began to write in the sand, paying no attention to the woman or those around Him. I was close enough that I could see what He was doing. He was writing a list of names, and beside each name He was writing a sin. By one He wrote "adultery." By another He wrote "blasphemy." By still another He wrote "thievery." And on and on. He listed the name of each man standing behind the woman. But the woman's name appeared nowhere on the list!

I wondered what would happen next. Was He going to accuse them? These were obviously sins these men would want to keep private. Not only would these sins be a great source of embarrassment, but if they were made public, they could cost these men their positions of influence. Perhaps some of them might even be stoned to death themselves.

The priest who had spoken continued to demand an answer. When Jesus looked up, He didn't look at the woman, He looked at the men and said, *"All right, but let the one who has never sinned throw the first stone!"* [2]

No one moved. They just stared at the writing in the sand. The men were restrained by their own guilt. After a few minutes, I heard the stones start falling to the ground. The men made no attempt to explain themselves but simply hurried away as if they had an important appointment.

Jesus stood up, looked at the woman, and asked, *"Woman, where are your accusers? Didn't even one of them condemn you?"* [3]

The woman replied in amazement, *"No, Lord."* [4] To which Jesus responded, *"Neither do I. Go and sin no more."* [5]

The men had fled in fear. But their fear had fled with them. What would happen if Jesus ever revealed what He knew about them? Each of these men was now even more committed to silencing Jesus.

∾

24

THE ENTRY OF THE KING AND A SURPRISING VOTE

~

hat brings us to the week that was unlike any other – the Passover celebration. Hordes of pilgrims gathered in Jerusalem; some having traveled for weeks to get there. Many had come for a reason other than Passover – they had come to see Jesus!

Word of His miracles had spread far and wide. Some people had come seeking a miracle for themselves, while others simply wanted to see Him perform a miracle. There was excitement in the air as everyone waited expectantly for His arrival.

It was the first day of the week and I was in the temple. Since Jesus had always entered the city quietly and come straight to the temple to teach, I decided if I was going to see Him, it would be there.

But soon I heard shouts echoing throughout the city. At first, it was cheers and an ever increasing clamor, but soon the shouts became a chant as the crowd yelled in unison, "Hosanna!" There was no doubt the people were heralding the arrival of Jesus!

I walked outside to observe. Surprisingly, the people were moving toward the eastern gate, which historically was used by kings and reserved for royalty. But then I realized how appropriate it was for Jesus to enter in through that gate.

Then I saw Him, riding on the back of a colt. Not only was He entering through the royal gate, but He was also riding in the style of a king. At that moment, the writing of the prophet Zechariah came to mind:

Look, your King is coming to you. He is righteous and victorious, yet He is humble, riding on a donkey – riding on a donkey's colt.[1]

I watched as several men placed their garments over the colt to make riding more comfortable for Jesus. People began to spread their garments on the road ahead of Him. Others laid down palm branches they had cut in nearby fields.

The crowd began to repeatedly shout, *"Praise God for the Son of David! Blessings on the One who comes in the name of the Lord! Praise God in highest heaven!"*[2] Some of the people standing around me were surprised when I added my voice to the refrain.

The cheers grew even louder as more people joined the procession. Soon it seemed the entire city was in an uproar. I noticed some of my fellow Sanhedrin brothers had also come out to see what the commotion was about. When they saw Jesus, they indignantly called out to Him, *"Teacher, rebuke Your followers for saying things like that!"*[3]

Jesus responded, *"If they kept quiet, the stones along the road would burst into cheers!"*[4] The men indignantly retreated back into the hall. I knew they were fearful that the crowd was preparing to crown Jesus as King.

When He arrived at the temple, Jesus dismounted the colt, and the crowd parted so He could enter. As He walked through the Court of the Gentiles, I saw Annas standing off in a corner with Caiaphas. They were watching Jesus's every move. Annas was speaking to the younger man in hushed tones, while Caiaphas nodded his head in agreement. Their smug expressions told me they were plotting something.

I expected Jesus to make His way to the court and begin teaching. But surprisingly, He did not. After spending some time walking around the temple in prayer, He departed – much more quietly than He had arrived. I expected I would see Him again the next day.

That evening Caiaphas sent word to all of us to gather in the great hall, though he did not explain why until after we arrived.

"The number of pilgrims pouring into the city is increasing with each day," he announced. "We have never seen so many people. The priests have advised us we must allow the merchants and the stables back into the outer court so they can accommodate the great need for animals to sacrifice and temple coins to exchange. They are fearful the stoa will be overrun, and the seriousness of the offerings and sacrifices will be interrupted.

"I know we have chosen not to do so for the past few years, but I fear we do not have a choice this year. Because we have been divided over this issue, I have called you together to put it to a vote. What say you?"

Several of us looked at one another in astonishment. How could Caiaphas even consider this proposal? Our members had consistently and overwhelmingly agreed to keep the animals and the merchants out of the courtyard. Why would he place it forward for a vote at such a late hour?

But it was I who was surprised, along with a few of my fellow council members, when the vote was overwhelmingly cast in favor of doing so! I suddenly realized the conviction of many of my Sanhedrin brothers had given way to their fear of Jesus. This vote was obviously for the sole purpose of creating a charge against Him.

25

JESUS CLEANSES THE TEMPLE ... AGAIN

~

I wanted to get word to Jesus about the vote and what was being set up in the temple, but I did not know where He was spending the night. At first, I worried what would happen when He walked into their trap. Then the Spirit of God calmed my heart, reminding me Jesus is the Son of God. He knew what these men were going to do – even before they knew themselves.

I made a point of arriving at the temple just as the sun rose. The stalls and tables were in place. The animals were in their stalls, and the merchants were attending to final details. Annas and Caiaphas were in the far corner of the courtyard making sure everything was in order.

As I walked past one of the stalls, the merchant recognized me as a member of the Sanhedrin. "Rabbi," he asked, "how does everything look to you? We didn't have much time to get this done. But we worked hard all through the night and did the best we could."

"I am sorry you had to work through the night," I replied.

"We are here to serve our leaders," he added, "and the people – and Jehovah God, of course. So, I want to be certain I serve well. That's why I asked if everything looked okay to you. Rabbi, can I ask you a question?"

"Yes, go right ahead."

He began somewhat tentatively. "How do you think Jesus is going to react when He arrives this morning? I was here when He chased us out three years ago. I saw His anger; but more importantly, I understood the reason for His anger. And then, a year ago, He healed my son. My child was lame, but Jesus enabled him to walk. I saw the tenderness of Jesus, and my heart affirmed His teaching to be true.

"Begging your pardon, I don't think Jesus was wrong to clear out the temple. I think what we are now doing is wrong. Please sir, I do not mean any disrespect, but I wondered what you think. How do you think Jesus will react?"

I answered him as honestly as I could. "I believe Jesus will act as Jehovah God would have Him act. I believe Jehovah God is sovereign over all things – even this decision. And I believe He will use it all for His glory. So, I will trust Him, no matter what happens – even when I don't understand. That is my word of counsel to you as well, my friend. Thank you for your service."

As I walked away, the merchant slowly nodded his head as he pondered what I had said.

Neither one of us had long to wait. Jesus arrived at the temple within the hour. As I suspected, He was not surprised by what He saw. The moment He stepped into the courtyard He shouted, "*It is written: 'My house will be a house of prayer.' But you have made it 'a den of robbers.'*"[1]

He immediately began turning over the tables and chairs, driving the merchants from the temple just as He had three years earlier. But this time the merchants were not surprised. They exited the court quickly and returned to their stalls and tables in the stoa. They knew they had been used as pawns in a game they did not understand.

I kept watching Annas and Caiaphas as this played out. They looked quite smug and victorious. Obviously, Jesus had reacted just as they expected. After the courtyard was cleared, Jesus continued into the temple with people following Him. Jesus received them all, healing them and teaching until He departed at the end of the day.

The next morning, Caiaphas and Annas asked their co-conspirators in the Sanhedrin to join them in the courtyard so they could confront Jesus when He arrived. As a part of the orchestrated plot, they acted shocked and offended by His actions. They voiced their objections to what He had done, saying He had completely undermined their authority. He had never once come to them seeking their approval for His actions.

As far as they were concerned, they had never delegated Him any authority, and He had ignored their official positions for far too long. They were now unified and emboldened by the fear they would lose their power over the people. Caiaphas spoke on their behalf: *"By what authority are You doing all these things? Who gave You the right to do them?"*[2]

But Jesus knew what was in their hearts. He wisely asked them, *"Did John's authority to baptize come from heaven, or was it merely human?"*[3]

Two years earlier, the baptizer had been arrested and beheaded by Herod Antipas. These same leaders had avoided having to confront him for what they viewed as his disrespect of their authority. I had often wondered what part they had played in his death. But Jesus was now forcing them to take a public stand regarding John.

They knew whatever answer they gave Jesus, the crowd would turn on them and they would lose their authority, position, and prestige. So, they refused to answer His question by pleading ignorance. That prompted Jesus to respond, *"Then I won't tell you by what authority I do these things."*[4]

The group turned and left in a huff with Caiaphas and Annas leading the way. They sequestered themselves behind closed doors – and away from piercing eyes – so they could discuss the next step in their twisted plot. I was not invited to join them. Neither was Joseph nor the others who had voiced opposition to their plan the night before.

26

A TUMULTUOUS TUESDAY THAT LED TO A QUIET THURSDAY

~

*N*ine of us had voted against bringing the merchants back into the temple. We all believed doing so was a desecration of the temple. Forty other members had once agreed with us, but their fear of Jesus had caused them to abandon their convictions.

Of the nine who remained, only Joseph and I truly believed Jesus to be the Son of God. The other seven, which included Gamaliel, had not yet come to that place. But we were all upset that Caiaphas was now excluding us from Sanhedrin meetings. The guards refused to let us enter the meeting hall.

Gamaliel pulled us aside and said, "The high priest has no legal authority to exclude us. A member can only be excluded if he is unseated. Unseating a member requires a vote of at least two-thirds of the entire Sanhedrin, and I know for a fact he is not able to garner that much support. This is an illegal action that must be confronted."

Gamaliel, a respected teacher, was not one to be trifled with. He sent messages to the influential members notifying them their assembly was illegal because they had excluded the nine of us. Caiaphas soon came out of the hall to see us.

"I apologize for any confusion, my brothers," he said. "I'm not sure why you were told you could not enter the hall. I will find out who was responsible for issuing that erroneous order to the guards. I can assure you they will be dealt with harshly. I had not noticed your absence, so thank you for bringing it to my attention. Please return to the hall with me so we can all proceed with the business at hand."

We knew none of that was true – except for the fact some guard would be punished for simply carrying out an order he had been given. When we took our seats, our fellow members feigned their extreme displeasure over how we had been mistreated. Caiaphas formally extended apologies to us and assured everyone the matter would be investigated and dealt with swiftly.

He then announced there would be no further action taken regarding the merchants or the placement of the stalls. They would remain outside in the stoa for the remainder of the Passover celebration. The council would revisit the matter at some future point.

No mention was made of Jesus or His actions in the temple that day or for the next two days. It was early Friday morning before we learned the members had voted during our absence to delegate twelve men to form a special high council under the leadership of Caiaphas. They had the responsibility and autonomy to take whatever action was necessary to eliminate Jesus as a threat to the Sanhedrin. Even though it was an illegal action since the nine of us were absent, no one ever spoke a word about it.

The next day, I saw this new group gathered in one of our smaller meeting rooms – Caiaphas, Annas, Ishmael ben Phabi, Eleazar, Simon, Jonathan, Theophilus, and six others. I knew they were discussing Jesus – but that wasn't unusual because that was all this group of men seemed to talk about these days.

I was surprised, however, to see a man I knew to be one of Jesus's disciples enter the room. I could not imagine why Jesus would send him to meet with these men. But He must have, I reasoned, since Jesus was there teaching in the courtyard.

The next day was Thursday, the day before the beginning of Passover. Jesus was conspicuously absent from the temple. The courtyard had been full of people anticipating His arrival, but they eventually drifted away as the day went on. It turned out to be an unusually quiet day, despite the record crowd gathered for Passover.

As I walked home, I couldn't shake the feeling that this was the lull before the storm. I was truly puzzled.

When I arrived home, I told Tali about Jesus's absence from the temple.

"I wonder what kept Him away?" she mused.

"I can't imagine," I responded. "Each day this week I have expected Him to declare to the people that He is the Messiah. They are ready to follow Him. They are just waiting for Him to say the word. I think many thought He might do so today on the eve of Passover. But obviously that wasn't His plan. Perhaps tomorrow will be the day."

∾

27

A SURPRISE ARREST

~

I settled into bed early that night. The first part of the week had weighed heavily on me, so I needed the rest. I fell into a deep sleep quickly and began dreaming I was on the shore of the Sea of Galilee. It was a bright day, and the seas were calm. But suddenly, a storm seemed to arise from nowhere. Gale force winds began to blow. The sea surged, and a wave started to crash over me. I heard Tali crying out to me from somewhere down shore.

I awoke with a start, drenched in perspiration. It had been a terrible dream – but gratefully, only a dream. However, I sensed someone standing near the edge of my bed. It was Tali, calling my name. That part hadn't been a dream.

"Nicodemus, get up!" she exclaimed. "You must get up! Joseph of Arimathea is here for you! You must get up and hear what he has to say!"

I opened my eyes and tried to clear the fog from my mind. I could see my wife was extremely upset. Something had happened – and my heart filled with dread.

"Nicodemus, you must hurry!" she said a little louder this time. "Joseph has important news for you."

"What is it, wife?" I asked as I tried to gather my senses.

"Something has happened to Jesus," she cried. "Joseph has come for you."

I was instantly awake. I jumped to my feet, threw on my cloak, and walked to our outer room to meet Joseph. I could see the worry written all over his face. "They have arrested Jesus!" he exclaimed.

"Who has arrested Jesus?" I asked.

"Caiaphas and Annas sent the temple guards together with several priests to arrest Him," he replied. "Jesus was in the Garden of Gethsemane with His disciples and the priests arrested Him. All of His disciples scattered and abandoned Him."

I could not believe what I was hearing. "They arrested Him? For what? And by whose authority?"

"Apparently the Sanhedrin voted on Tuesday while we were kept out of the hall to establish a special council that was given complete authority to do whatever was needed to eliminate Jesus as a threat. They have accused Him of blasphemy against God and sedition against Rome," Joseph explained. "They mean to have Him crucified."

"They mean to do what?" I implored. "That can't be possible! Have they gone mad? The council is illegal. They were chosen and empowered by an illegal vote. This must be stopped!"

Joseph knew we needed to act and not waste time talking. "Nicodemus, get dressed," he said sternly. "They are holding Jesus in the cell beneath Caiaphas's home. We must go now and see if we can talk some sense into them!"

When we arrived at the high priest's home, no one tried to prevent us from entering. Out of the corner of my eye, I noticed my nephew John standing by the window. "What is he doing here?" I wondered.

Before Joseph and I could ask any questions, Caiaphas addressed us. "A few moments ago, in this very room with all of these witnesses gathered, Jesus publicly declared Himself to be the Son of God! Earlier this week, we all heard the crowds refer to Him as King and Jesus made no attempt to correct them. As a matter of fact, He was heard to say, *'I tell you, if these were silent, the very stones would cry out.'*[1]

"By virtue of His declaration before all these witnesses, no further proof is required. A simple majority of the Sanhedrin is all that is needed to convict Him. The forty men who heard His proclamation unanimously voted to convict Him of blasphemy, and we have enough evidence to bring a charge of sedition before Pontius Pilate. We are planning to take Jesus to the praetorium to stand before Pilate even now. The matter is done. It's out of our hands!"

"What do you mean the matter is done and it's out of our hands?" I cried out. "It's very much in your hands! You and the others have set this in motion. Jesus is guilty of nothing, other than being the Promised One sent by God. He *is* the Son of God! I know it's true –and you know it's true."

"I know no such thing!" Caiaphas responded in a calm but stern voice. "And I would advise you to remain silent or this council will charge you with blasphemy!"

A man near the back of the room moved, and I recognized him as the disciple I had previously seen meeting with Caiaphas and the others. *"I have sinned,"* he shouted, *"for I have betrayed an innocent man."*[2]

"What do we care?" Annas retorted. *"That's your problem."*[3] Caiaphas motioned to the temple guards to remove him.

All of a sudden, the man threw pieces of silver on the floor and stormed from the room. It was apparently blood money they had given him for betraying Jesus. Caiaphas directed one of the servants to pick up the coins. Earlier during the week, one of our discussions in the hall had centered around what to do with foreigners who die in Jerusalem.

Seeing the coins on the floor, Caiaphas declared, *"It wouldn't be right to put this money in the temple treasury.*[15] Use it to buy a field that can be used as a cemetery for the burial of foreigners. Call it the 'Field of Blood.' Now guards, make ready the prisoner. We will leave now to deliver Him to Pilate."

Caiaphas brushed past Joseph and me as he left the room. The two of us stood there, not knowing what we should do. I turned and saw my nephew still standing by the window.

~

28

"IT IS FINISHED!"

∽

*J*ohn turned to us and began to explain. "Earlier this evening, Jesus announced that Judas was going to betray Him, but we didn't completely understand what He meant. We never imagined Jesus would be arrested – nor, in our wildest dreams, did we imagine He would be condemned to death. It all happened so quickly. I am ashamed to tell you we all ran in fear when they came to arrest Jesus. Not one of us stood by His side!"

John was weeping as he gave his account. He was broken over what was happening to Jesus – but also over his own failing. "Is there anything that can be done to stop this?" he asked desperately.

Neither Joseph nor I knew what to do at this point. But I still hoped God the Father would intervene for His Son. "Not once Pilate issues His death decree," I said. "Hopefully, he will see that Jesus has not done anything worthy of crucifixion. Joseph and I will go to the praetorium and see if we can convince Caiaphas to stop this madness!"

"I will go and find Jesus's mother," John replied. "I'm sure the others have already told her what has happened, but she will want to see Him, and I do not want her to do that alone."

When Joseph and I arrived at the praetorium, we found out that Pilate had already referred the charges against Jesus to Herod Antipas. Pilate decided that since Jesus was a Galilean and Herod was the governor over Galilee, he should determine Jesus's fate. But before we arrived at Herod's palace, we saw Jesus being taken back to stand before Pilate once again. Apparently, Herod had deferred the matter back to the Roman prefect since Jesus had been arrested in Judea.

Everything happened swiftly! Before we knew it, Pilate declared Jesus guilty despite his own protests to the contrary. He even went through a show of washing his hands of Jesus's blood. Had the entire world gone mad?

Now that the death order had been issued, we knew there was nothing anyone could do – short of a pardon from Caesar himself. Jesus was going to be crucified today. My mind couldn't comprehend it!

Joseph and I watched as members of the high council made their way to Golgotha to witness the crucifixion. I could not bring myself to follow them. I returned home where Tali and I wept for Jesus. We wept for His mother and His disciples. But we also wept for our people. God had sent His Son and we had rejected Him! His blood would forever be on our hands!

At noon, the sky turned black – day had become night. Surely it was a sign of the judgment awaiting us for what our people were doing to God's Son. Then a thought crossed my mind. The law precluded an honorable burial for one who was executed for violating the law. Jesus's body would be left hanging on the cross overnight in disgrace. There was no way I could permit that to happen to the body of my Lord.

I was certain His family and His disciples had not thought about this; they were overwhelmed by everything else happening. Whatever was to be done would need to happen quickly before sunset and the beginning of Sabbath.

I went to find Joseph to discuss what we could do. When I arrived at his home, I discovered he had already come to the same conclusion. We decided we first needed to go to Pilate and request Jesus's body. We were hoping Annas and Caiaphas had not done anything to block His body from being buried.

When we arrived at the praetorium, Pilate came outside to receive us. "I am told you want to bury the body of Jesus," he said with surprise. "Is that correct?"

"Yes, it is," we replied.

"How can that be when it was you religious leaders who demanded His death?" he asked.

"The two of us did not demand His death," I said. "He is an innocent Man. He has not done anything worthy of death!"

"I agree with you," Pilate replied. "But Caiaphas and Annas were adamant – and the crowd all shouted in agreement."

Pilate seemed to be seeking our forgiveness for his role in Jesus's death. He was looking to wash away the guilt he felt. We, however, stood in silence. We would not help him justify his part in this travesty of justice. Eventually, he gave us a document granting us permission to receive Jesus's body once He was declared dead.

Joseph had recently acquired a tomb intended for his own burial, but he offered to let us bury Jesus's body in his tomb. We stopped at one of the shops in the city and purchased a linen shroud and the ointments we would need to prepare His body for burial.

We were horrified to see what had been done to Jesus when we arrived at the foot of His cross. The torture and pain they had inflicted to His body was obvious. Just then we heard Him say, *"It is finished!"*[1]

We both fell to our knees and wept. When we regained our composure, we approached the Roman centurion with the document Pilate had given us. There was also another man at the foot of the cross. We had seen him when we arrived. As we prepared to take Jesus's body to the tomb, he came to us and said, "I carried His cross to Golgotha, and now I will carry His body to the tomb."

As the three of us placed Jesus's body in the tomb and sealed it with a great stone, a group of Roman soldiers appeared. Evidently, Caiaphas and Annas had petitioned Pilate to post guards so no one could remove His body and declare that Jesus had risen from the grave.

∼

29

THE TOMB IS EMPTY!

~

I was back home with Tali just as night began to fall. The two of us were reeling from the events of the past twenty-four hours. Jesus was dead! I had held His lifeless body in my arms as we laid Him in the tomb. How could it be?

I knew Jesus was the Son of the Living God. He was the Promised Messiah. He was the One whose coming was foretold by the prophets. He was the One who would set us free! But His own people had rejected Him. Most of our religious leaders had been complicit in His death!

I reflected on all the prophecies I had heard. Since I was a boy, I had anticipated His arrival much like the generations before me. I thought everyone was looking forward to His coming. He was to establish His kingdom and rule over us. Had we somehow foiled God's plan by murdering His Son? That had never been part of the prophecies I remembered nor was it something we talked about in synagogue or in the School of Hillel.

My mind was racing. Was there anything about the Messiah dying in the writings of any of the prophets? It was then God brought to mind these words from the prophet Isaiah:

He was despised and rejected — a man of sorrows, acquainted with deepest grief. We turned our backs on Him and looked the other way. He was despised, and we did not care. Yet it was our weaknesses He carried; it was our sorrows that weighed Him down.

And we thought His troubles were a punishment from God, a punishment for His own sins!

Or so Caiaphas and the others wanted us to believe. But Jesus was without sin, and Jehovah God had already set the record straight through the prophecy:

He was pierced for our rebellion, crushed for our sins. He was beaten so we could be whole. He was whipped so we could be healed.

I had seen the stripes on His flesh from being whipped. I had seen the opening in His side from being pierced by the spear. I had seen the bruises all over His body from being beaten by the Roman soldiers.

All of us, like sheep, have strayed away. We have left God's paths to follow our own. Yet the Lord laid on Him the sins of us all. He was oppressed and treated harshly,

yet He never said a word. He was led like a lamb to the slaughter. And as a sheep is silent before the shearers, He did not open His mouth. Unjustly condemned,

He was led away. No one cared that He died without descendants, that His life was cut short in midstream. But He was struck down for the rebellion of My people. He had done no wrong and had never deceived anyone …

Today that prophecy had been fulfilled. He had been slaughtered for the sins of us all. He was unjustly condemned … but willingly faced the punishment as our Passover Lamb. He was sent by the Father to be the spotless Passover Lamb whose blood had now been shed as a covering for our sins. How fitting that God had allowed this to occur on the very day that our people remember the Passover lamb.

And then I remembered the last words of that prophecy:

... but He was buried like a criminal; He was put in a rich man's grave.[1]

Unbeknownst to Joseph and me, we had fulfilled those words just moments ago. How many times had I read or heard those words? Today I had seen them come to pass. It was my own iniquity that led Jesus to the cross today. I couldn't blame Annas, or Caiaphas, or Pilate alone. It was the sinfulness of us all. As that reality flooded my mind and heart, I began to weep uncontrollably.

I wept throughout that night, the next day, and into the third day. That afternoon there was a knock on our door. To my surprise, it was my nephew, John. But instead of looking heartbroken, his face was radiant with joy!

"Uncle Nicodemus, Jesus is alive!" he exclaimed. "I have been to the tomb. His body is not there! He has risen from the grave! He had told us He would – but we had not understood. Now, He has appeared to many of our number this morning and this afternoon. Rejoice, Uncle ... Jesus is alive!"

I wanted to rejoice – but it was all so difficult to comprehend. For two days I had been consumed by grief, but now John was saying Jesus had conquered death and the grave. We all knew He had raised others from the dead, but now He Himself had walked out of the tomb!

I thought about the soldiers who had arrived at the tomb as Joseph and I were leaving. What must they have thought when they saw Jesus walk out of that grave!?!

"Uncle," John continued, "Jesus said we should all gather in the room over the home of Yitzhak the merchant. Get dressed and come with me."

"You go ahead!" I told him. "I will go and find Joseph and the man who carried Jesus's body to the tomb – the one named Simon. I will tell them what you have said, and we will all come to the upper room."

I did just that. When we arrived at the upper room, several men and women were excitedly telling us about seeing Jesus that day. All at once, Jesus appeared in our midst! I saw Him standing before us with my own eyes. Jesus is alive!

∾

30

I NOW KNOW WHAT I HAVE TO DO!

~

The next day, Joseph and I walked into the Hall of Hewn Stones together. The other members were already in their places discussing the news that Jesus had risen from the grave.

"We feared the disciples of Jesus would do something like this," Caiaphas said. "That's why we petitioned Pilate to post guards at the tomb. But by their own admission, the guards fell asleep. Yesterday they told us Jesus's disciples came while they were sleeping and stole His body.

"No resurrection has taken place – only an attempt at deception. The guards are searching the surrounding area to find out where His body has been placed. Brothers, I would admonish each of you to squelch this false rumor at every opportunity. Jesus is not alive! He has been crucified, and He is dead! God has punished Him for His sins."

I could no longer listen to these lies!

"My Sanhedrin brothers, I have come to tell you that Jesus is, in fact, alive!" I blurted out. "Joseph and I saw Him last evening and spoke with Him in this very city!"

An uproar immediately arose in the hall. Some were shouting to drown out my words while others shouted because they wanted to hear more. I waited for the noise to die down.

"Our leaders want us to believe the disciples of Jesus are attempting to deceive us," I continued. "In reality, it is our leaders who are attempting to deceive us. The same men who orchestrated the plot to have Him crucified now stand before you denying the truth of His resurrection.

"Each of you has witnessed the miracles He performed. Each of you has heard the words He taught. Many of you were involved in trying to discredit Him in some way – but all those attempts failed. And they failed because He is who He said He is. You may deny it with your words, but you cannot deny it with your hearts.

"When Jesus told us three years ago that if we destroyed the temple, He would raise it up in three days, He was talking about Himself. He knew the sin and wickedness and deceit in our hearts. He knew we would ulti-mately orchestrate the events of this past Friday – and He was telling us even then He would rise from the dead."

Some of the men began shouting again to keep me from speaking further, but this time it was quite a few members who quieted them down. "Let Nicodemus finish!" they shouted.

"Jesus was the slain Lamb Isaiah foretold," I continued. "But He is not one of many lambs who must be slain for our sin, He is the one and only Lamb. And though His blood was shed, He alone has conquered death and the grave. He is a Living Sacrifice. He is the sacrifice God promised on this very hill to our Father Abraham many years ago when he was prepared to sacrifice his own son, Isaac. Jehovah God has sacrificed His own Son. But He who died for us is now alive. The prophecy is completed!"

As I looked around the room, I saw a handful of members carefully considering my words. But I could tell by their angry faces that the majority was refusing to accept the truth.

"That is a very interesting story, Nicodemus," Caiaphas began. "It is very creative. It is the kind of story you would make up to tell children. But we are not children. We are the religious leaders of our people, and we have done what needed to be done. No one has returned from the dead. Even the ones Jesus supposedly raised from the dead were merely tricks intended to deceive us."

"Be careful, Caiaphas," I said, "one of those you refer to is my grand-daughter. And I can assure you she was raised from the dead just as Jesus has been raised from the dead!"

"Nicodemus," Caiaphas continued in a condescending tone, "I have no doubt you believe that – but you have been deceived. I will no longer stand here and argue with you. I cannot permit a member of this Sanhedrin to embrace such heresy against God and such disrespect against our leadership. According to the laws of our land, I place the question before this body – should Nicodemus be discharged from his position on this Sanhedrin?"

Joseph interrupted, saying, "Caiaphas, I echo everything Nicodemus has said. I, too, have seen the risen Jesus. He is alive and He is my Lord and Savior. If you discharge Nicodemus, then you must discharge me as well!"

Caiaphas looked amazed. Then he shook his head and said, "Members, you have heard Joseph. What say you, should Nicodemus and Joseph both be discharged?"

By an overwhelming margin, Joseph and I were discharged from the Sanhedrin that day. Several men did not vote in agreement, which made them suspect among the others. One of them, my friend Gamaliel, would one day stand up for Jesus himself.

That day was the first of many in which God would lead me to take a stand for my Lord and Savior. I remained in Jerusalem for the next fifty days leading up to the Feast of Pentecost, experiencing snubs and ridicule from many of those with whom I had served. But in their stead, we found fellowship with those like us who had become followers of Jesus. Tali and I stood on the hill outside the city with many of them the day Jesus ascended into heaven to sit at the right hand of the Father.

And the two of us, together with Joseph, were back in the upper room over Yitzhak's home when the Holy Spirit came upon us all ten days after Jesus ascended. Soon afterward, Tali and I left Jerusalem. We returned home to Capernaum to bear witness throughout Galilee and Samaria to the words Jesus spoke to me that night long ago:

As Moses lifted up the bronze snake on a pole in the wilderness, so Jesus was lifted up on the cross, *so that everyone who believes in Him will have eternal life."* [1]

∾

PLEASE HELP ME BY LEAVING A REVIEW!

i would be very grateful if you would leave a review of this book. Your feedback will be helpful to me in my future writing endeavors and will also assist others as they consider picking up a copy of the book.

To leave a review:

Go to: amazon.com/dp/1736715593

Or scan this QR code using your camera on your smartphone:

Thanks for your help!

～

THE COMPLETE SERIES

… you will want to read all of the books in "The Called" series

Experience the stories of these ordinary men and women who were called by God to be used in extraordinary ways through this series of first-person biblical fiction novellas.

A Carpenter Called Joseph (Book 1)

A Prophet Called Isaiah (Book 2)

A Teacher Called Nicodemus (Book 3)

A Judge Called Deborah (Book 4) - releasing May 20

A Merchant Called Lydia (Book 5) - releasing July 22

A Friend Called Enoch (Book 6) - releasing Fall 2022

Available through Amazon.

Scan this QR code using your camera on your smartphone to see the entire series on Amazon:

THE EYEWITNESSES COLLECTION

... you will also want to read "The Eyewitnesses" Collection

The first four books in these collections of short stories chronicle the first person eyewitness accounts of eighty-five men, women and children and their unique relationships with Jesus. You'll hear from some of the characters you met in *"A Teacher Called Nicodemus"* and learn more about their stories.

Little Did We Know – the advent of Jesus (Book 1)

Not Too Little To Know – the advent – ages 8 thru adult (Book 2)

The One Who Stood Before Us – the ministry and passion of Jesus (Book 3)

The Little Ones Who Came – the ministry and passion – ages 8 thru adult (Book 4)

The Patriarchs — eyewitnesses from the beginning — Adam through Moses tell their stories (Book 5) — releasing in 2023

Now available through Amazon.

Scan this QR code using your camera on your smartphone to see the entire collection on Amazon:

THROUGH THE EYES SERIES

... the other books in the *"THROUGH THE EYES"* SERIES

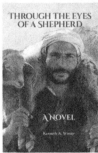  

Experience the truths of Scripture as these stories unfold through the lives and eyes of a shepherd, a spy and a prisoner. Rooted in biblical truth, these fictional novels will enable you to draw beside the storytellers as they worship the Baby in the manger, the Son who took up the cross, the Savior who conquered the grave, the Deliverer who parted the sea and the Eternal God who has always had a mission.

Through the Eyes of a Shepherd (Book 1)

Through the Eyes of a Spy (Book 2)

Through the Eyes of a Prisoner (Book 3)

Now available through Amazon.

Scan this QR code using your camera on your smartphone to see the entire series on Amazon:

LESSONS LEARNED IN THE WILDERNESS SERIES

The Lessons Learned In The Wilderness series

A non-fiction series of devotional studies

There are lessons that can only be learned in the wilderness experiences of our lives. As we see throughout the Bible, God is right there leading us each and every step of the way, if we will follow Him. Wherever we are, whatever we are experiencing, He will use it to enable us to experience His Person, witness His power and join Him in His mission.

The Journey Begins (Exodus) – Book 1

The Wandering Years (Numbers and Deuteronomy) – Book 2

Possessing The Promise (Joshua and Judges) – Book 3

Walking With The Master (The Gospels leading up to Palm Sunday) – Book 4

Taking Up The Cross (The Gospels – the passion through ascension) – Book 5

Until He Returns (The Book of Acts) – Book 6

The complete series is also available in two e-book boxsets or two single soft-cover print volumes.

Now available through Amazon.

Scan this QR code using your camera on your smartphone to see the entire series on Amazon:

For more information, go to:

wildernesslessons.com or kenwinter.org

ALSO AVAILABLE AS AN AUDIOBOOK

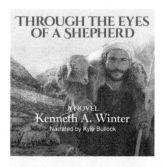

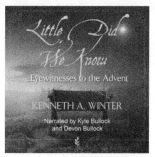

SCRIPTURE BIBLIOGRAPHY

~

Much of the story line of this book is taken from the Gospel according to John. Certain fictional events or depictions of those events have been added.

Some of the dialogue in this story are direct quotations from Scripture. Here are the specific references for those quotations:

Preface

[1] John 3:16

[2] John 7:51-52

[3] John 19:38-42

Chapter 2

[1] Psalm 100:1-5

Chapter 4

[1] Exodus 20: 2, 3, 6 (NASB)

Chapter 5
(1) Isaiah 61:1

Chapter 8
(1) Genesis 2:18 (HCSB)

(2) Job 1:21

(3) Psalm 23:4 (paraphrase)

Chapter 10
(1) Example of dispute taken from Deuteronomy 22:13-19

Chapter 14
(1) John 1:21

(2) John 1:22

(3) John 1:23

(4) Matthew 3:7-8, 11-12

Chapter 16
(1) John 2:16

Chapter 17
(1) John 2:18

(2) John 2:18

(3) John 2:19

(4) John 2:20

(5) Psalm 69:9

Chapter 18

(1) John 1:36

(2) Mark 1:11

Chapter 19

(1) John 3:2

(2) John 3:3

(3) John 3:4

(4) John 3:5-6

(5) John 3:9

(6) John 3:10-15

(7) John 3:16-17

(8) John 3:18-21

Chapter 20

(1) John 3:21

(2) Jeremiah 29:13

Chapter 21

(1) Luke 2:34-35 (CEV – paraphrase)

(2) Luke 2:29-30 (CEV)

Chapter 22

(1) John 4:50

(2) Mark 5:23

(3) Mark 5:35

(4) Mark 5:36

(5) Mark 5:39

(6) Mark 5:41

Chapter 23

(1) John 8:4

(2) John 8:7

(3) John 8:10

(4) John 8:11

(5) John 8:11

Chapter 24

(1) Zechariah 9:9

(2) Matthew 21:9

(3) Luke 19:39

(4) Luke 19:40

Chapter 25

(1) Luke 19:46 (ESV)

(2) Mark 11:28

(3) Mark 11:30

Chapter 27

(1) Luke 19:40

(2) Matthew 27:4

(3) Matthew 27:4

(4) Matthew 27:6

Chapter 28

(1) John 19:30

Chapter 29

[1] Isaiah 53:3-9

Chapter 30

[1] John 3:15

~

LISTING OF CHARACTERS
(ALPHABETICAL ORDER)

～

Many of the characters in this book are real people pulled directly from the pages of Scripture. i have not changed any details about those individuals except in some instances their interactions with the fictional characters. They are noted below as "UN" (unchanged).

In other instances, fictional details have been added to real people to provide additional background about their lives where Scripture is silent. The intent is to provide further information for the story. They are noted as "FB" (fictional background).

In some instances, we are never told the names of certain individuals in the Bible. In those instances, where i have given them a name as well as a fictional background, they are noted as "FN" (fictional name).

Lastly, a few of the characters are purely fictional, added to convey the fictional elements of these stories . They are noted as "FC" (fictional character).

～

Adir – great-great-grandfather of Nicodemus (FC)
Andrew - brother of Simon Peter, friend of John, disciple of Jesus (UN)

Annas - high priest 6-15AD (FB)

Asher - grandfather of Nicodemus (FC)

Ashriel – great-grandson of Simeon, rabbi in Arimathea (FC)

Betzalel - a carpenter, father of Jairus (FC)

Caiaphas - high priest 18-36AD, son-in-law of Annas (FB)

Camydus – brother of Hillel & Shebna, grandfather of Annas (FC)

Devorah - wife of Adir (FC)

Eleazar ben Annas - son of Annas, High Priest 17-17AD, member of Sanhedrin (FB)

Gamaliel - member of Sanhedrin, grandson of Hillel (FB)

Herod, the Great - the tetrarch (UN)

Herod Antipas – sixth son of Herod the Great, ethnarch over Galilee and Perea (UN)

Hillel, the Elder - respected teacher, brother of Shebna & Camydus, grandfather of Gamaliel (FB)

Ilana - daughter of Jairus and Leah, granddaughter of Nicodemus, raised from the dead by Jesus (FN)

Ishmael - son of Shebna, business partner of Yaakov, father of Salome and Tali (FC)

Ishmael ben Phabi - High Priest 15-16AD, member of Sanhedrin (FB)

Jairus - rabbi in Capernaum, father of Ilana (FB)

James - son of Zebedee and Salome, disciple of Jesus (UN)

Jesus - Son of the Living God (UN)

John - son of Zebedee and Salome, disciple of Jesus (FB)

John the baptizer – a voice crying in the wilderness preparing the way (UN)

Jonah - father of Simon Peter and Andrew, fishing partner of Zebedee (UN)

Jonathan ben Annas - son of Annas, High Priest 36-37AD, member of Sanhedrin (FB)

Joseph of Arimathea - pharisee, member of Sanhedrin (FB)

Judas Maccabeus - led the revolt against the Seleucid Empire (FB)

Leah - daughter of Nicodemus and Tali, wife of Jairus, mother of Ilana (FC)

Marianne - wife (3rd) of Herod the Great, daughter of Simon ben Boethus (UN)

Mattathias Maccabeus – father of Judas Maccabeus (UN)

Matthew - tax collector in Capernaum, disciple of Jesus (UN)

Menahem - great-grandfather of Nicodemus, son of Adir (FC)

Nahum - GGG-grandfather of Nicodemus, fought with Judas Maccabeus in revolt, namesake of Capernaum (FC)

Nicodemus – rabbi, member of the Sanhedrin (FB)

Nissa - daughter of Shebna, younger sister of Ishmael, wife of Yaakov, mother of Nicodemus (FC)

Pontius Pilate – Roman prefect of Judea (UN)

Rebekah - daughter of Nicodemus and Tali (FC)

Reuben - son of Nicodemus (FC)

Salome - daughter of Ishmael, sister of Tali, wife of Zebedee, mother of James & John (FB)

Shebna - brother of Hillel & Camydus, business partner of Asher, father of Ishmael (FC)

Simeon - the ancient who God promised would see the Messiah (UN)

Simon ben Boethus - High Priest 23-5 B.C. (UN)

Simon ben Camithus - High Priest 17-18 A.D., member of Sanhedrin (FB)

Simon Peter - son of Jonah, disciple of Jesus (UN)

Simon the Cyrene - pulled from crowd to carry the cross of Jesus (FB)

Tali - wife of Nicodemus, daughter of Ishmael, sister of Salome (FC)

Theophilus ben Annas – son of Annas, High Priest 37-41AD, member of Sanhedrin (FB)

Unnamed father in case heard by local Sanhedrin (FC)

Unnamed husband in case heard by local Sanhedrin (FC)

Unnamed merchant in the temple (FC)

Unnamed priest who accused the adulterous woman (FB)

Unnamed wife in case heard by local Sanhedrin (FC)

Uriah – son of Yitzhak (FC)

Yaakov - father of Nicodemus, son of Asher, business partner of Ishmael (FC)

Yitzhak – merchant in Jerusalem, owner of the upper room used by Jesus (FC)

Zebedee - husband of Salome, father of James & John, fishing partner with Jonah and later Simon Peter (UN)

∾

ACKNOWLEDGMENTS

I do not cease to give thanks for you ....
Ephesians 1:16 (ESV)

… my partner in all things, LaVonne,
for choosing to trust God as we follow Him in this faith adventure
together;

… my family,
for your love, support and encouragement;

… Sheryl,
for enabling me to tell the story in a better way;

… Scott,
for the way you use your creative gifts to bring glory to God;

… a great group of friends who have read an advance copy of this book,
for all of your help, feedback and encouragement;

… and most importantly,
the One who is truly the Author and Finisher of it all
– our Lord and Savior Jesus Christ!

~

ABOUT THE AUTHOR

Ken Winter is a follower of Jesus, an extremely blessed husband, and a proud father and grandfather – all by the grace of God. His journey with Jesus has led him to serve on the pastoral staffs of two local churches – one in West Palm Beach, Florida and the other in Richmond, Virginia – and as the vice president of mobilization of the IMB, an international missions organization.

Today, Ken continues in that journey as a full-time author, teacher and speaker. You can read his weekly blog posts at kenwinter.blog and listen to his weekly podcast at kenwinter.org/podcast.

And we proclaim Him, admonishing every man and teaching every man with all wisdom, that we may present every man complete in Christ. And for this purpose also I labor, striving according to His power, which mightily works within me.
(Colossians 1:28-29 NASB)

PLEASE JOIN MY READERS' GROUP

Please join my Readers' Group in order to receive updates and information about future releases, etc.

Also, i will send you a free copy of *The Journey Begins* e-book — the first book in the *Lessons Learned In The Wilderness* series. It is yours to keep or share with a friend or family member that you think might benefit from it.

It's completely free to sign up. i value your privacy and will not spam you. Also, you can unsubscribe at any time.

Go to kenwinter.org to subscribe.

Or scan this QR code using your camera on your smartphone:

Made in the USA
Monee, IL
03 September 2022

13189736R00080